McGRAW-HILL READING

Spelling

Grade 1   Practice Book

McGraw-Hill
School Division
New York   Farmington

CONTENTS

Book 1.1

Book 1.2

One Good Pup
Words with Short *u*

The Bug Bath
Words with Short *o*

Splash!
Words with Short *e*

What Bug Is It?
Words with Blends

A Vet
Words from Social Studies

Book 1.3

Book 1.4

The Shopping List
Words with Long *i: i-e*

Yasmin's Ducks
Words with Long *o: o-e*

The Knee-High Man
Words with Long *u: u-e*

Johnny Appleseed
Words with Long *a: ai, ay*

Ring! Ring! Ring! Put Out the Fire!
Words from Social Studies

Book 1.5 / Unit 1

Book 1.5 / Unit 2

Name_____ Date_____ **Spelling**  **1**

Words with Short *a*

Complete each word by writing the letter that spells
the short *a* sound.

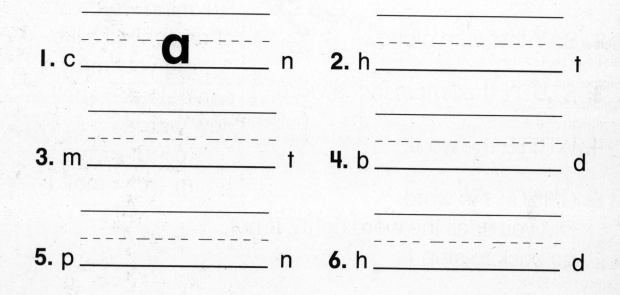

1. c _____ n   2. h _____ t

3. m _____ t   4. b _____ d

5. p _____ n   6. h _____ d

Directions (to teacher)

Review the short a sound by explaining that the letter *a* stands for /a/ as in
the word *can*. Write *can* on the chalkboard or form the word with letter cards.
Say the word aloud and have children repeat it. Then have children look at
the first example on the page. Point out that the letter *a* has been filled in.

Write the words *can, hat, mat, bad, pan,* and *had* on the chalkboard. Read
the words aloud and have children repeat them. Have children listen for the
short *a* sound in each word. Then have them complete each word in the
space provided.

Words with Short *a*

Using the Word Study Steps

1. LOOK at the word.

2. SAY the word aloud.

3. STUDY the letters in the word.

4. WRITE the word.

5. CHECK the word.
   Did you spell the word right? If not,
   go back to step 1.

Spelling Tip

Rhyming words are often spelled alike. A word you know can help you spell new words.

c + at = cat
m + at = mat

Word Scramble

Unscramble each set of letters to make a spelling word.

1. anc _____

2. pna _____

3. abd _____

4. tha _____

5. hda _____

6. tam _____

To Parents or Helpers:
 Using the Word Study Steps above as your child comes across any new words will help him or her spell well. Review the steps as you both go over this week's spelling words.
 Go over the Spelling Tip with your child. Ask if he or she knows other words that rhyme with the spelling words. Help your child write new words that rhyme with the word he or she wants to spell.
 Help your child complete the spelling activity.

Words with Short *a*

Look at the spelling words in the box.

can hat mat bad pan had

Write the words that end with **an**.

1. _____   2. _____

Write the words that end with **at**.

3. _____   4. _____

Write the words that end with **ad**.

5. _____   6. _____

Words with Short *a*

Look at the picture. Add **an** or **at** or **ad** to complete the word.

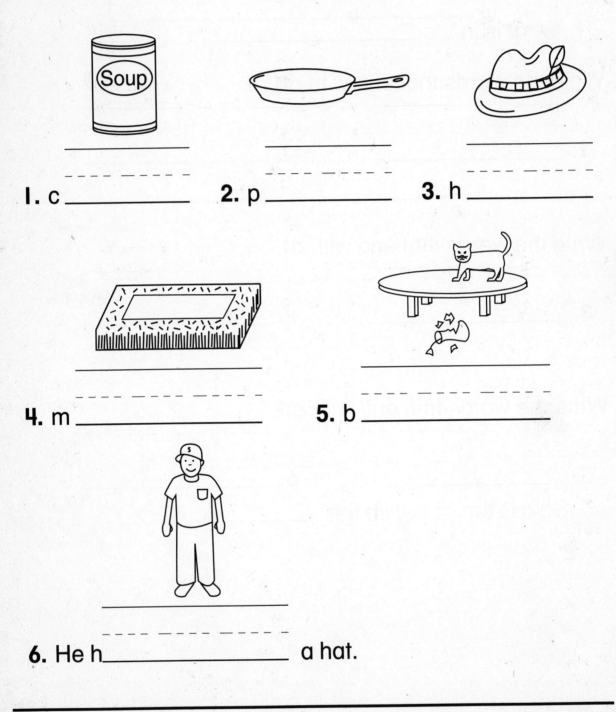

1. c _____

2. p _____

3. h _____

4. m _____

5. b _____

6. He h _____ a hat.

Words with Short *a*

Look at the picture. Complete each sentence
with a spelling word.

1. What is in the _____?

2. That cat is _____!

3. Max can nap on a _____.

4. That cat _____ nap on a cap!

5. Sam is the man with the _____.

6. Pam _____ a cat.

Words with Short *a*

Look at the words in each set. One word in each set is spelled correctly. Use a pencil to color in the circle in front of that word. Before you begin, look at the sample sets of words. Sample A has been done for you. Do Sample B by yourself. When you are sure you know what to do, you may go on with the rest of the page.

Sample A
- (A) has
- (B) haz
- (C) haas

Sample B
- (D) cat
- (E) catt
- (F) kat

1. (A) paan
   (B) pann
   (C) pan

2. (D) faen
   (E) fann
   (F) fan

3. (A) cann
   (B) can
   (C) kan

4. (D) hat
   (E) het
   (F) hatt

5. (A) matt
   (B) nat
   (C) mat

6. (D) hadd
   (E) had
   (F) dah

Words with Digraph *ck*

Complete each word by writing the letters *ck*
on the line.

1. ba __**ck**_____   2. pa _____

3. qua _____   4. ra _____

5. sa _____   6. ta _____

Directions (to teacher)

Display the word *back* on the chalkboard or with letter cards. Explain
that the letters ck spell the sound /k/. Say the word aloud and have
children repeat it. Then have them look at the first example on the
page. Point out that the letters *ck* have been filled in.

Write the words *pack, quack, rack, sack,* and *tack* on the
chalkboard. Read the words aloud and have children repeat them.
Have them listen for the sound /k/ in each word. Then have them
complete each word in the space provided.

Words with Digraph ck

Using the Word Study Steps

1. LOOK at the word.

2. SAY the word aloud.

3. STUDY the letters in the word.

4. WRITE the word.

5. CHECK the word.
   Did you spell the word right? If not,
   go back to step 1.

Spelling Tip

The letter **q** is always
followed by **u**.
quack

Find and Circle

Where are the spelling words?

c b b a c k q p a c k

h q u a c k s r a c k

s a c k q a c t a c k

To Parents or Helpers:
Using the Word Study Steps above as your child comes across any new words will help him or her spell well. Review the steps as you both go over this week's spelling words.
Go over the Spelling Tip with your child. Help your child write new words in which the letter q is followed by the letter u.
Help your child find and circle the spelling words in the puzzle.

Words with Digraph ck

Connect each word part with the ending **ack** to
make a spelling word. Write the spelling words on
the lines.

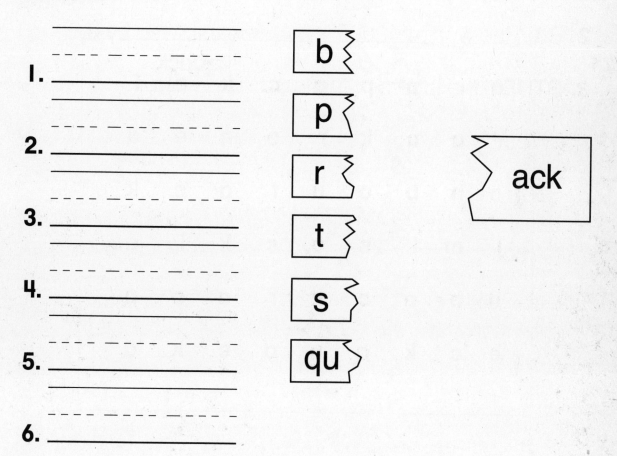

I. _____

2. _____

3. _____

4. _____

5. _____

6. _____

Words with Digraph ck

Look at the spelling words in the box. Find the spelling words in the puzzle. Draw a circle around each word.

```
a   r   p   p   a   c   k   e   l
r   a   c   k   r   o   n   e   a
o   h   b   o   u   t   a   c   k
l   m   l   s   a   c   k   l   a
d   b   a   c   k   r   a   o   p
e   c   k   q   u   a   c   k   d
```

Words with Digraph ck

Look at the picture. Complete each sentence with a spelling word.

1. Nan sat at the _____ .

2. Jack has his _____ .

3. The _____ is in the van.

4. My hat is on the _____ .

5. The duck said, " _____ " .

6. Look out for the _____ !

Words with Digraph ck

Look at the words in each set. One word in each set is spelled correctly. Use a pencil to color in the circle in front of that word. Before you begin, look at the sample sets of words. Sample A has been done for you. Do Sample B by yourself. When you are sure you know what to do, you may go on with the rest of the page.

Sample A
- Ⓐ bat
- Ⓑ batt
- Ⓒ baat

Sample B
- Ⓓ cann
- Ⓔ kan
- Ⓕ can

1. Ⓐ quak
　　Ⓑ qack
　　Ⓒ quack

2. Ⓓ rac
　　Ⓔ rak
　　Ⓕ rack

3. Ⓐ sak
　　Ⓑ sack
　　Ⓒ sacc

4. Ⓓ pak
　　Ⓔ pack
　　Ⓕ pac

5. Ⓐ back
　　Ⓑ bak
　　Ⓒ baak

6. Ⓓ tack
　　Ⓔ takc
　　Ⓕ tac

Words with Short i

Complete each word by writing the letter that spells the short **i** sound.

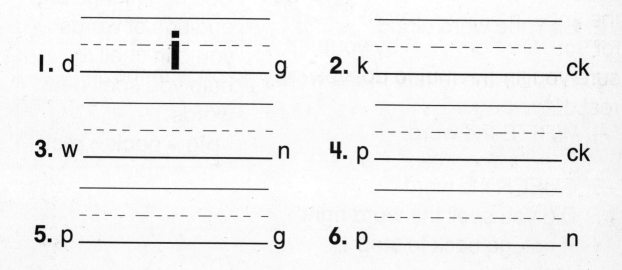

1. d _____**i**_____ g   2. k _____ ck

3. w _____ n   4. p _____ ck

5. p _____ g   6. p _____ n

Directions (to teacher)

Review the short *i* sound by explaining that the letter *i* stands for /i/ as in the word *dig*. Write *dig* on the chalkboard or form the word with letter cards. Say the word aloud and have children repeat it. Then have them look at the first example on the page. Point out that the letter *i* has been filled in.

Write the words *kick, win, pick, pig,* and *pin* on the chalkboard. Read the words aloud and have children repeat them. Have them listen for the short *i* sound in each word. Then have them complete each word in the space provided.

Words with Short i

Using the Word Study Steps

1. LOOK at the word.

2. SAY the word aloud.

3. STUDY the letters in the word.

4. WRITE the word.

5. CHECK the word.
   Did you spell the word right?
   If not, go back to step 1.

Spelling Tip

Use beginnings and endings of words you can spell to help you spell new words.

pig + pa**ck** = **pick**

Fill in the Blank

Write the spelling word that best fits each sentence.

1. I _____ the ball.

2. I _____ a flower.

3. I _____ in the sand.

4. A _____ is on a farm.

5. Did you _____ the race?

6. I need a _____ to sew.

To Parents or Helpers:
    Using the Word Study Steps above as your child comes across any new words will help him or her spell well. Review the steps as you both go over this week's spelling words.
    Go over the Spelling Tip with your child. Help your child write new words that use beginnings and endings of words he or she can spell.
    Help your child complete the spelling activity.

Words with Short i

Look at the spelling words in the box.

> **dig   kick   win   pick   pig   pin**

Write the words that end with **in**.

1._____   2._____

Write the words that end with **ig**.

3._____   4._____

Write the words that end with **ick**.

5._____   6._____

Words with Short i

Look at each picture. Add **in** or **ig** or **ick** to complete the word.

_____
- - - - - - - - - -
I. p_____

_____
- - - - - - - - - -
2. d_____

_____
- - - - - - - - - -
3. k_____

Use the other three spelling words to complete the sentences.

_____
- - - - - - - - -
The man will p _____ a pig.

_____
- - - - - - - - - -
He will give the pig a p_____ and say,

_____
- - - - - - - - -
"You w _____!"

Words with Short i

Look at the picture. Complete each sentence
with a spelling word.

_____
- - - - - - - - - -
1. Mom can _____ a hole.

_____
- - - - - - - - - -
2. _____ up the cap, Mack.

_____
- - - - - - - - - -
3. Dan can _____ the ball.

_____
- - - - - - - - - -
4. They _____ the game!

_____
- - - - - - - - - -
5. The _____ is big.

_____
- - - - - - - - - -
6. Can you fix the hat with a _____ ?

Words with Short i

Look at the words in each set. One word in each set is spelled correctly. Use a pencil to color in the circle in front of that word. Before you begin, look at the sample sets of words. Sample A has been done for you. Do Sample B by yourself. When you are sure you know what to do, you may go on with the rest of the page.

Sample A
- (A) big
- (B) bigg
- (C) biig

Sample B
- (D) pac
- (E) pack
- (F) pakc

1. (A) pig
   (B) pigg
   (C) gip

2. (D) pick
   (E) pic
   (F) pik

3. (A) dig
   (B) digg
   (C) gid

4. (D) kik
   (E) kic
   (F) kick

5. (A) winn
   (B) win
   (C) wiin

6. (D) pin
   (E) ppin
   (F) pinn

Words with Digraphs sh, th

Complete each word by writing the letters **sh** or **th**
on the line.

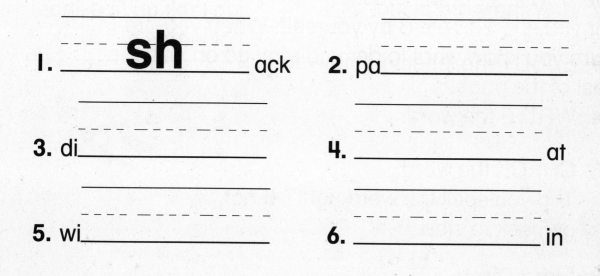

1. _____ **sh** _____ ack   2. pa_____

3. di_____   4. _____ at

5. wi_____   6. _____ in

Directions (to teacher)

Review the digraph *sh* by explaining that the letters *sh* stand for /sh/ as in the
word *shack*. Write *shack* on the chalkboard or with letter cards. Say the word
aloud and have children repeat it. Then have them look at the first example on
the page. Point out that the letters *sh* have been filled in.

Write the word *path* on the chalkboard. Read the word aloud and have children
repeat it. Tell them that the letters th stand for the sound /th/. Have them
compete the word by writing *th* on the line provided. Point out that the letters th
come at the end of the word.

Write *dish, that, thin* and *wish* on the chalkboard. Read each word aloud and
have children repeat it. Have them listen for the sound /sh/ or /th/. Then have
children complete the words on the lines provided.

Words with Digraphs sh, th

Using the Word Study Steps

1. LOOK at the word.

2. SAY the word aloud.

3. STUDY the letters in the word.

4. WRITE the word.

5. CHECK the word.
   Did you spell the word right? If not,
   go back to step 1.

Spelling Tip

Use the dictionary to look up spellings of words.

Find and Circle

Where are the spelling words?

```
s p a t h w s h a c k

t h d i s h a t h a t

w i s h d t h i n s h
```

Parents or Helpers:

   Using the Word Study Steps above as your child comes across any new words will help him or her spell well. Review the steps as you both go over this week's spelling words.
   Go over the Spelling Tip with your child. Help your child use the dictionary to look up spellings of words.
   Help your child find and circle the spelling words in the puzzle.

Words with Digraphs sh, th

Look at the spelling words in the box.

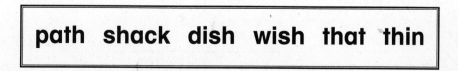

path shack dish wish that thin

Write the words that have **sh**. Circle **sh** in each word.

1. _____

2. _____

3. _____

Write the words that have **th**. Circle **th** in each word.

4. _____

5. _____

6. _____

Words with Digraphs sh, th

Look at the picture. Add **sh** or **th** to
complete the word.

1. _____ ack   2. _____ op   3. di _____

4. pa _____   5. _____ in   6. wi _____

Words with Digraphs sh, th

Look at the picture. Complete each sentence
with a spelling word.

1. The _____ is on the map.

2. This fish is _____ .

3. No one is in the _____ .

4. I will pick _____ cat.

5. The _____ is on the rack.

6. Will Ann get her _____ ?

Words with Digraphs sh, th

Look at the words in each set. One word in each set is spelled correctly. Use a pencil to color in the circle in front of that word. Before you begin, look at the sample sets of words. Sample A has been done for you. Do Sample B by yourself. When you are sure you know what to do, you may go on with the rest of the page.

Sample A
- Ⓐ fish
- Ⓑ fihs
- Ⓒ fis

Sample B
- Ⓓ pigg
- Ⓔ pig
- Ⓕ piig

1. Ⓐ ttat
   Ⓑ that
   Ⓒ thatt

4. Ⓓ shak
   Ⓔ shack
   Ⓕ shac

2. Ⓓ wish
   Ⓔ wihs
   Ⓕ wis

5. Ⓐ dihs
   Ⓑ dis
   Ⓒ dish

3. Ⓐ path
   Ⓑ phath
   Ⓒ patt

6. Ⓓ tinn
   Ⓔ thinn
   Ⓕ thin

Words from Social Studies

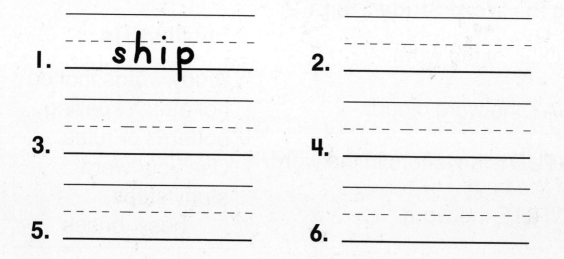

1. ship

2. _____

3. _____

4. _____

5. _____

6. _____

Directions (to teacher)

Write the words ship, stop, go, bus, fast, and map on the chalkboard. Have children find the word ship filled in on this page. Read the word aloud and have them repeat it.

Tell children they will be writing each of the other five words on this page. Read each word aloud. Have children repeat it and write it in the blank provided.

You may also wish to present the challenge words look, this, one, and what.

Name_____ Date_____

Words from Social Studies

Using the Word Study Steps

1. LOOK at the word.

2. SAY the word aloud.

3. STUDY the letters in the word.

4. WRITE the word.

5. CHECK the word.
   Did you spell the word right? If not,
   go back to step 1.

> ### Spelling Tip
>
> Study words that do not match spelling patterns or rules. Use your word study steps.
>
> bus = buses

X the Word

In each row put an X on the word that does not belong.

1.	ship	cup	boat
2.	one	two	stop
3.	go	mat	no
4.	bus	car	fish
5.	slow	big	fast
6.	dog	map	cap

To Parents or Helpers:
Using the Word Study Steps above as your child comes across any new words will help him or her spell well. Review the steps as you both go over this week's spelling words.
    Go over the Spelling Tip with your child. Help your child use the word study steps to study words that do not match spelling patterns or rules.
    Help your child complete the spelling activity.

Words from Social Studies

Look at the spelling words in the box. Write each spelling word on the line where it belongs.

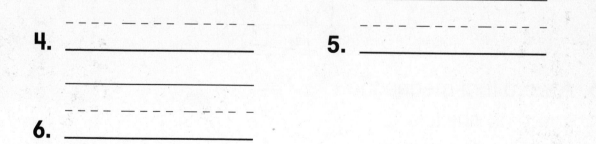

ship stop go bus fast map

Write the spelling word with two letters.

1. _____

Write the spelling words with three letters.

2. _____   3. _____

Write the spelling words with four letters.

4. _____   5. _____

6. _____

Words from Social Studies

Find pictures for the spelling words. Write the words on the lines.

1. _____

2. _____

3. _____

4. _____

5. _____

6. A word that means the same as quick is

_____.

Words from Social Studies

Look at the picture. Complete each sentence
with a spelling word.

1. We look at a _____.

2. We see a _____.

3. The bus can _____.

4. There is a _____.

5. Look, we can _____ now.

6. The boy can run _____.

Name_____ Date_____

Words from Social Studies

Look at the words in each set. One word in each set is spelled correctly. Use a pencil to color in the circle in front of that word. Before you begin, look at the sample sets of words. Sample A has been done for you. Do Sample B by yourself. When you are sure you know what to do, you may go on with the rest of the page.

Sample A
- (A) one
- (B) wun
- (C) onne

Sample B
- (D) shac
- (E) shak
- (F) shack

1. (A) fas
   (B) fast
   (C) fass

2. (D) buz
   (E) buse
   (F) bus

3. (A) goe
   (B) gow
   (C) go

4. (D) stap
   (E) stop
   (F) stopp

5. (A) shipp
   (B) ship
   (C) shipe

6. (D) map
   (E) mapp
   (F) mep

Unit Review Test

Read each sentence. If an underlined word is spelled wrong, fill in the circle that goes with that word. If no word is spelled wrong, fill in the circle below NONE.

Read Sample A, and do Sample B.

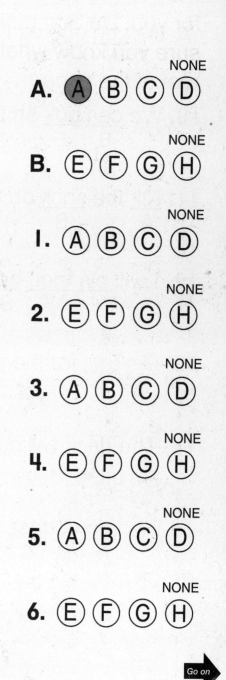

A. The <u>doge</u> <u>had</u> a <u>nap</u>.
  A   B   C

B. <u>Sam</u> <u>satt</u> in a <u>van</u>.
  E   F   G

1. I <u>can</u> <u>pack</u> my <u>hatt</u>.
  A   B   C

2. We <u>go</u> <u>fast</u> on the <u>buss</u>.
  E   F   G

3. She will <u>kick</u> <u>that</u> <u>sacke</u>.
  A   B   C

4. He <u>can</u> <u>go</u> on the <u>pathh</u>.
  E   F   G

5. It is <u>baad</u> to <u>kick</u> the <u>hat</u>.
  A   B   C

6. I <u>wishe</u> for <u>that</u> <u>hat</u>.
  E   F   G

NONE
A. Ⓐ Ⓑ Ⓒ Ⓓ

NONE
B. Ⓔ Ⓕ Ⓖ Ⓗ

NONE
1. Ⓐ Ⓑ Ⓒ Ⓓ

NONE
2. Ⓔ Ⓕ Ⓖ Ⓗ

NONE
3. Ⓐ Ⓑ Ⓒ Ⓓ

NONE
4. Ⓔ Ⓕ Ⓖ Ⓗ

NONE
5. Ⓐ Ⓑ Ⓒ Ⓓ

NONE
6. Ⓔ Ⓕ Ⓖ Ⓗ

Go on ➡

7. The man will <u>go</u> to <u>digg</u> a <u>path</u>.
              A   B   C

NONE
7. Ⓐ Ⓑ Ⓒ Ⓓ

8. I <u>wish</u> I <u>can</u> <u>quak</u>.
    E   F   G

NONE
8. Ⓔ Ⓕ Ⓖ Ⓗ

9. He <u>can</u> <u>goe</u> on the <u>bus</u>.
    A   B   C

NONE
9. Ⓐ Ⓑ Ⓒ Ⓓ

10. We <u>can</u> <u>pak</u> on the <u>bus</u>.
    E   F   G

NONE
10. Ⓔ Ⓕ Ⓖ Ⓗ

11. <u>Kik</u> the <u>sack</u> on the <u>path</u>.
   A   B   C

NONE
11. Ⓐ Ⓑ Ⓒ Ⓓ

12. I will <u>pin</u> <u>thatt</u> <u>hat</u>.
       E   F   G

NONE
12. Ⓔ Ⓕ Ⓖ Ⓗ

13. <u>Dig</u> <u>fast</u> for the <u>pinn</u>.
   A   B   C

NONE
13. Ⓐ Ⓑ Ⓒ Ⓓ

14. The <u>duck</u> will <u>quack</u> in the <u>sack</u>.
      E   F   G

NONE
14. Ⓔ Ⓕ Ⓖ Ⓗ

15. He <u>can</u> <u>go</u> <u>fasst</u>.
     A   B C

NONE
15. Ⓐ Ⓑ Ⓒ Ⓓ

Words with Short *u*

Complete each word by writing the letter that spells the short *u* sound.

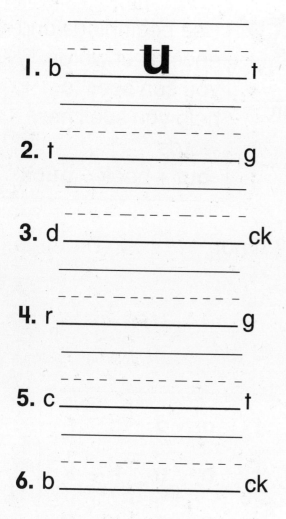

1. b_____ **u** _____t

2. t_____g

3. d_____ck

4. r_____g

5. c_____t

6. b_____ck

Directions (to teacher)

Review the short *u* sound by explaining that the letter *u* stands for /u/ as in the word *but*. Write *but* on the chalkboard or form the word with letter cards. Say the word aloud and have children repeat it. Then have children look at the first example on the page. Point out that the letter *u* has been filled in.

Write the words *cut, tug, rug, duck,* and *buck* on the chalkboard. Read each word aloud and have children repeat it. Have them listen for the short u sound in each word. Then have them complete each word in the blank provided.

Name_____ Date_____

Words with Short u

Using the Word Study Steps

1. LOOK at the word.

2. SAY the word aloud.

3. STUDY the letters in the word.

4. WRITE the word.

5. CHECK the word.
   Did you spell the word right? If not,
   go back to step 1.

> ### Spelling Tip
> Use beginnings and endings of words you can spell to help you spell new words.
>
> **bu**t + ba**ck** = **buck**

Find and Circle
Where are the spelling words?

b	u	c	k	c	u	t	a	d	o	r
o	d	u	c	k	p	r	b	u	t	k
r	t	u	g	t	h	e	p	r	u	g

To Parents or Helpers:
   Using the Word Study Steps above as your child comes across any new words will help him or her spell well. Review the steps as you both go over this week's spelling words.
   Go over the Spelling Tip with your child. Help your child write new words in different ways to see which one looks right.
   Help your child find and circle the spelling words in the puzzle.

Words with Short *u*

Complete the spelling words inside each dog bone.
Put the words with the same endings in the same box.

but tug duck rug cut buck

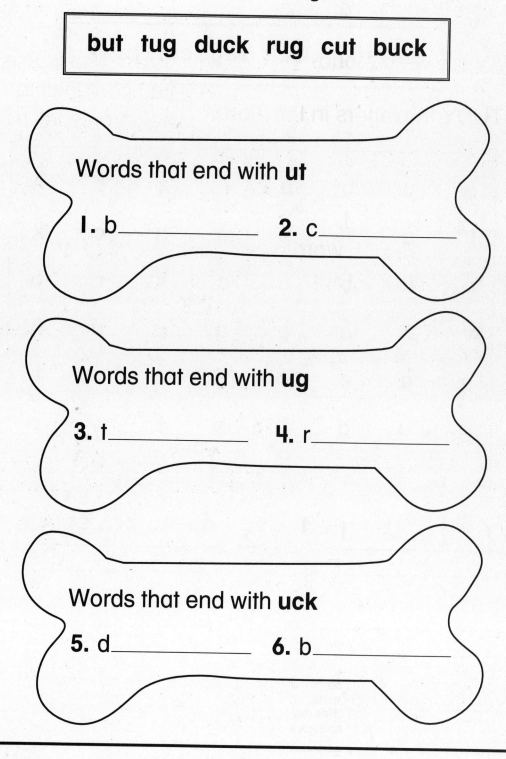

Words that end with **ut**

1. b_____ 2. c_____

Words that end with **ug**

3. t_____ 4. r_____

Words that end with **uck**

5. d_____ 6. b_____

Words with Short *u*

Read the words in the box. Circle the words in the puzzle. Then write the words on the lines.

but tug duck rug cut buck

q	u	b	u	t	z	d	e
l	a	t	s	d	u	c	k
u	k	b	u	c	k	r	a
v	t	u	g	g	u	u	h
n	e	c	o	n	c	u	t
r	u	g	l	s	t	y	o

1. _____

2. _____

3. _____

4. _____

5. _____

6. _____

Words with Short *u*

Look at the picture. Complete each sentence with a
spelling word.

1. Do not _____ your hand!

2. The cat sits on the _____ .

3. The _____ said, "Quack."

4. Do not _____ the pup!

5. The _____ ran up
   the path.

6. I wish to go out, _____
   it is so wet!

Words with Short u

Look at the words in each set. One word in each set is spelled correctly. Use a pencil to color in the circle in front of that word. Before you begin, look at the sample sets of words. Sample A has been done for you. Do Sample B by yourself. When you are sure you know what to do, you may go on with the rest of the page.

Sample A

Ⓐ bug

Ⓑ bugg

Ⓒ buug

Sample B

Ⓓ diss

Ⓔ dish

Ⓕ dihs

1. Ⓐ rugg

   Ⓑ rug

   Ⓒ ruug

4. Ⓓ dukk

   Ⓔ duc

   Ⓕ duck

2. Ⓓ buck

   Ⓔ buk

   Ⓕ buc

5. Ⓐ bot

   Ⓑ buut

   Ⓒ but

3. Ⓐ cut

   Ⓑ kut

   Ⓒ kutt

6. Ⓓ tugg

   Ⓔ tug

   Ⓕ tuug

Words with Short *o*

Complete each word by writing the letter that spells the short o sound.

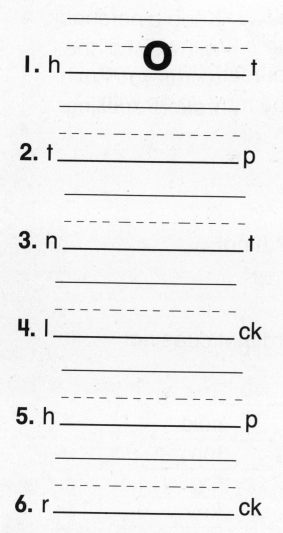

1. h_____ **O** _____t

2. t_____p

3. n_____t

4. l_____ck

5. h_____p

6. r_____ck

Directions (to teacher)

Review the short *o* sound by explaining that the letter *o* stands for /o/ as in the word *hot*. Write hot on the chalkboard or form the word with letter cards. Say the word aloud and have children repeat it. Then have children look at the first example on the page. Point out that the letter *o* has been filled in.

Write the words *top, not, lock, hop,* and *rock* on the chalkboard. Read the words aloud and have children repeat them. Have children listen for the short o sound in each word. Then, have them complete each word in the space provided.

Words with Short *o*

Using the Word Study Steps

1. LOOK at the word.

2. SAY the word aloud.

3. STUDY the letters in the word.

4. WRITE the word.

5. CHECK the word.
Did you spell the word right? If not,
go back to step 1.

Spelling Tip

Keep a notebook with a list of the words you have trouble spelling.

X the word

In each row, put an X on the word that does not belong.

1.	bug	hot	cold
2.	mop	wish	top
3.	pot	not	tag
4.	lock	hat	key
5.	hop	skip	that
6.	sock	tap	rock

To Parents or Helpers:

Using the Word Study Steps above as your child comes across any new words will help him or her spell well. Review the steps as you both go over this week's spelling words.

Go over the Spelling Tip with your child. Help your child write words that they have trouble spelling in a notebook that they can keep. Help your child complete the spelling activity.

Words with Short o

Put each bug in the right tub. Write the words with
the same endings in the same tub.

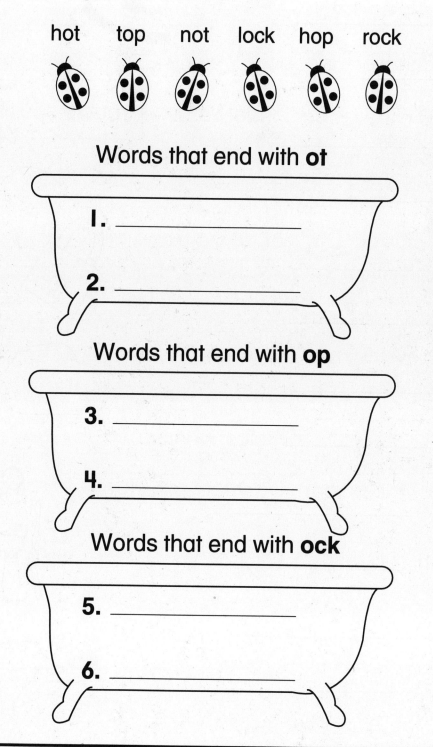

hot   top   not   lock   hop   rock

Words that end with ot

1. _____

2. _____

Words that end with op

3. _____

4. _____

Words that end with ock

5. _____

6. _____

Words with Short o

Look at the picture. Add **ot** or **op** or **ock** to complete the word.

1. t _____

2. h _____

3. l _____

4. r _____

5. It is h _____ .

6. It is n _____ .

Words with Short o

Look at the picture. Complete the sentence with a
spelling word. _____

1. The logs are _____.

2. She can _____.

3. I can _____ the door.

4. Do you have the _____
for this pan?

5. The bug is on the _____.

6. Write a sentence that uses the word not.
_____
_____
_____

Words with Short o

Look at the words in each set. One word in each set is spelled correctly. Use a pencil to color in the circle in front of that word. Before you begin, look at the sample sets of words. Sample A has been done for you. Do Sample B by yourself. When you are sure you know what to do, you may go on with the rest of the page.

Sample A
- (A) pot
- (B) pott
- (C) ppot

Sample B
- (D) duck
- (E) duc
- (F) duk

1. (A) hop
   (B) hopp
   (C) hoppe

4. (D) top
   (E) topp
   (F) toppe

2. (D) locke
   (E) lok
   (F) lock

5. (A) nott
   (B) not
   (C) noot

3. (A) hott
   (B) hot
   (C) hote

6. (D) roc
   (E) rok
   (F) rock

Name_____ Date_____

Words with Short *e*

Complete each word by writing the letter that spells the short e sound.

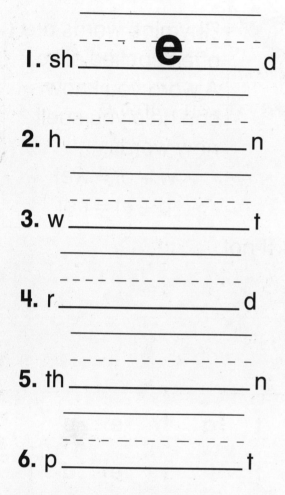

1. sh _____ **e** _____ d

2. h _____ n

3. w _____ t

4. r _____ d

5. th _____ n

6. p _____ t

Directions (to teacher)

Review the short *e* sound by explaining that the letter *e* stands for /e/ as in the word *shed*. Write *shed* on the chalkboard or form the word with letter cards. Say the word aloud and have children repeat it. Then have children look at the first example on the page. Point out that the letter e has been filled in.

Write the words *hen, wet, red, then,* and *pet* on the chalkboard. Read the words aloud and have children repeat them. Have children listen for the letter that stands for the short e sound in each word. Then have them complete each word.

Words with Short *e*

Using the Word Study Steps

1. LOOK at the word.

2. SAY the word aloud.

3. STUDY the letters in the word.

4. WRITE the word.

5. CHECK the word.
   Did you spell the word right? If not,
   go back to step 1.

Spelling Tip

Rhyming words are often spelled alike. A word you know can help you spell new words.

w + et = wet
p + et = pet

Find and Circle

Where are the spelling words?

u	t	s	h	e	d	t	a	h	e	n
o	d	u	c	w	e	t	l	r	e	d
r	t	h	e	n	h	e	p	e	t	g

Words with Short e

Add the ending **et** or **ed** or **en** to each letter to make a word from the box. Then write the spelling word.

| pet then hen red shed wet |

1. p + _____ = _____

2. w + _____ = _____

3. r + _____ = _____

4. sh + _____ = _____

5. h + _____ = _____

6. th + _____ = _____

Words with Short e

Draw a line to connect each word beginning with
the right ending to make a spelling word.
Then write the words.

1. _____

2. _____

3. _____

r < < et

th < < ed

w < < en

Complete these sentences with a spelling word.

4. The _____ like to
   eat corn.

5. They all love their
   _____ .

6. The two _____ are
   packed.

Words with Short *e*

Look at the picture. Complete each sentence with a
spelling word. _____

- - - - - - - - - - - - - - -
1. This cat is my _____ .

_____
- - - - - - - - - - - - - - -
2. Sam fed the _____ .

_____
- - - - - - - - - - - - - - -
3. The dog is in the _____ .

_____
- - - - - - - - - - - - - - -
4. Stop when it is _____ .

_____
- - - - - - - - - - - - - - -
5. Kim got _____ in the rain.

_____
- - - - - - - - - - - - - - -
6. It was raining, but _____
the sun came out.

Words with Short e

Look at the words in each set. One word in each set is spelled correctly. Use a pencil to color in the circle in front of that word. Before you begin, look at the sample sets of words. Sample A has been done for you. Do Sample B by yourself. When you are sure you know what to do, you may go on with the rest of the page.

Sample A

Ⓐ get
Ⓑ gett
Ⓒ geet

Sample B

Ⓓ rok
Ⓔ roc
Ⓕ rock

1. Ⓐ redd
Ⓑ red
Ⓒ rede

4. Ⓓ henn
Ⓔ hen
Ⓕ henne

2. Ⓓ wette
Ⓔ weet
Ⓕ wet

5. Ⓐ then
Ⓑ thenn
Ⓒ theen

3. Ⓐ pet
Ⓑ pett
Ⓒ ppet

6. Ⓓ shedd
Ⓔ shede
Ⓕ shed

Words with Blends

Complete each word by writing the letters **sn**, **fl**, **ss**, **ll**, or **ff** on the line.

1. ___**sn**___ ap

2. _____ at

3. pa _____

4. mi _____

5. do _____

6. pu _____

Directions (to teacher)

Review the blend *sn* by explaining that the letters *sn* spell the sounds /s/ and /n/, which may come together at the beginning of a word. Write *snap* on the chalkboard or form the word with letter cards. Say the word aloud and have children repeat it. Then have children look at the first example on the page. Point out that the letters *sn* have been filled in.

Display the word *flat*. Say the word aloud and have children repeat it. Have them listen for the two beginning sounds /f/ and /l/. Then have children complete the second example.

Display the word *pass*. Have children listen for the consonant sound at the end of the word (/s/). Tell them it is written with two of the same letter (s). Have them complete the third example.

Write the words *miss, doll,* and *puff* on the chalkboard. Read the words aloud and have children repeat them. Have children listen for the consonant sound at the end of each word. Tell children each is written with two of the same letter. Have children complete each word on the line provided.

Words with Blends

Using the Word Study Steps

1. LOOK at the word.

2. SAY the word aloud.

3. STUDY the letters in the word.

4. WRITE the word.

5. CHECK the word.
   Did you spell the word right?
   If not, go back to step 1.

Spelling Tip

Think of times when you have seen the word. Maybe you have read it in a book or on a sign. Try to remember how it looked. Write the word in different ways to see which one looks correct.
~~dol, dool,~~ doll

Word Scramble

Unscramble each set of letters to make a spelling word.

1. pasn _____

2. sims _____

3. oldl _____

4. alft _____

5. sasp _____

6. fupf _____

To Parents or Helpers:
Using the Word Study Steps above as your child comes across any new words will help him or her spell well. Review the steps as you both go over this week's spelling words.
Go over the Spelling Tip with your child. Help your child write new words in different ways to see which one looks right.
Help your child complete the spelling activity.

Words with Blends

Look at the spelling words in the box.

snap pass flat doll miss puff

Write the word that begins with **sn.**

1. _____

Write the word that begins with **fl.**

2. _____

Write the words that end with two letters that are the same.

3. _____   4. _____

5. _____   6. _____

Words with Blends

Look at the spelling words in the box. Then read the story below. Complete each spelling word.

snap pass flat doll miss puff

Jill has a do _____ . She calls it

Mi _____ Nell. The doll is _____ at,

but it has a big pu _____ of hair. It has a hat.

The hat can _____ ap on. Jill said to Max,

"Pa _____ me Miss Nell."

Words with Blends

Look at the picture. Complete each sentence with a spelling word.

1. Can you _____ your fingers?

2. The tire is _____ .

3. My _____ has a red dress.

4. Please _____ me the dish.

5. "I will huff and _____ !" said the big bad wolf.

6. Hit the ball! Do not _____ that ball!

Name_____ Date_____

Words with Blends

Look at the words in each set. One word in each set is spelled correctly. Use a pencil to color in the circle in front of that word. Before you begin, look at the sample sets of words. Sample A has been done for you. Do Sample B by yourself. When you are sure you know what to do, you may go on with the rest of the page.

Sample A

(A) bell

(B) bel

(C) bbel

Sample B

(D) cat

(E) catt

(F) kat

1. (A) mis

   (B) misse

   (C) miss

2. (D) doll

   (E) dol

   (F) dolle

3. (A) snape

   (B) snapp

   (C) snap

4. (D) pas

   (E) pass

   (F) passe

5. (A) filat

   (B) flatt

   (C) flat

6. (D) puuf

   (E) puff

   (F) puf

Words from Social Studies

1. 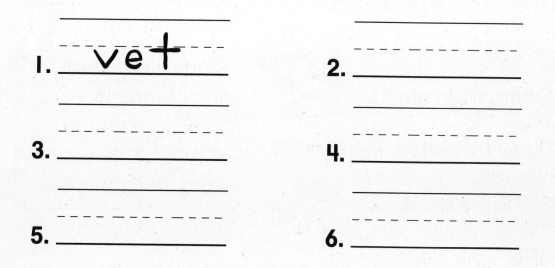 vet

2. _____

3. _____

4. _____

5. _____

6. _____

Directions (to teacher)
Write the words *vet, hog, cat, help, job,* and *pat* on the chalkboard. Have children find the word *vet* filled in on this page. Read the word aloud and have them repeat it.

Tell children they will be writing the other five words on this page. Read each word aloud. Have children repeat it and write it in the blank provided.

You may also wish to present the challenge words *small, out, good,* and *wants*.

Words from Social Studies

Using the Word Study Steps

1. LOOK at the word.

2. SAY the word aloud.

3. STUDY the letters in the word.

4. WRITE the word.

5. CHECK the word.
   Did you spell the word right? If not, go back to step 1.

> **Spelling Tip**
>
> Study words that do not match spelling patterns or rules. Use your word study steps.

Fill in the Blank

Write the spelling word that best fits each sentence.

1. I have a pet _____.

2. I _____ with the work.

3. I did a good _____.

4. His dog is at the _____.

5. A _____ eats a lot.

6. You _____ the puppy.

To Parents or Helpers:
    Using the Word Study Steps above as your child comes across any new words will help him or her spell well. Review the steps as you both go over this week's spelling words.
    Go over the Spelling Tip with your child. Help your child use the word study steps to study words that do not match spelling patterns or rules.
    Help your child complete the spelling activity.

Words from Social Studies

Write each spelling word on the line where it belongs.
Look at the spelling words in the box.

vet hog cat help job pat

Write the spelling words that have short **a** spelled **a.**

1. _____   2. _____

Write the spelling words that have short **e** spelled **e.**

3. _____   4. _____

Write the spelling words that have short **o** spelled **o.**

5. _____   6. _____

Words from Social Studies

Find the spelling words in the puzzle. Circle the words you find. Then write them on the lines below.

vet hog cat help job pat

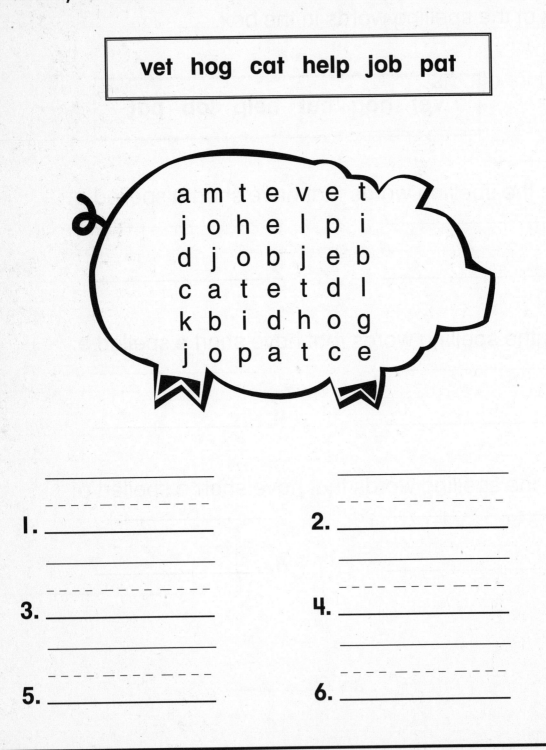

1. _____

2. _____

3. _____

4. _____

5. _____

6. _____

Words from Social Studies

Look at the pictures. Complete each spelling word.

1. The v _____ takes
   care of pets.

2. His j _____ is to
   care for sick pets.

3. The vet can _____ p
   big pets and small pets.

4. He likes to _____ at
   the horse.

5. He can look at a sick

   h _____ .

6. He helped this c _____
   get well.

Words from Social Studies

Look at the words in each set. One word in each set is spelled correctly. Use a pencil to color in the circle in front of that word. Before you begin, look at the sample sets of words. Sample A has been done for you. Do Sample B by yourself. When you are sure you know what to do, you may go on with the rest of the page.

Sample A
- (A) then
- (B) thenn
- (C) tenn

Sample B
- (D) flatt
- (E) flat
- (F) flatte

1. (A) catt
   (B) kat
   (C) cat

4. (D) helb
   (E) help
   (F) hellp

2. (D) hog
   (E) hogg
   (F) hoog

5. (A) vett
   (B) vete
   (C) vet

3. (A) jobb
   (B) jorb
   (C) job

6. (D) pat
   (E) patte
   (F) patt

Book 1.2 Unit Review Test

Read each sentence. If an underlined word is spelled wrong, fill in the circle that goes with that word. If no word is spelled wrong, fill in the circle below NONE.

Read Sample A, and do Sample B.

A. <u>Max</u> was a <u>tan</u> <u>catt</u>.
    A   B C

NONE
A. Ⓐ Ⓑ ●C Ⓓ

B. <u>That</u> was a <u>bad</u> <u>wishe</u>.
    E   F   G

NONE
B. Ⓔ Ⓕ Ⓖ Ⓗ

1. The <u>henn</u> is <u>wet</u> <u>but</u> not cold.
     A   B   C

NONE
1. Ⓐ Ⓑ Ⓒ Ⓓ

2. <u>Lock</u> her <u>dol</u> in the <u>shed</u>.
    E   F   G

NONE
2. Ⓔ Ⓕ Ⓖ Ⓗ

3. The <u>hoge</u> and <u>duck</u> are in the <u>shed</u>.
     A   B   C

NONE
3. Ⓐ Ⓑ Ⓒ Ⓓ

4. The <u>hot</u> <u>rug</u> is like a <u>puffe</u>.
     E F   G

NONE
4. Ⓔ Ⓕ Ⓖ Ⓗ

5. That <u>ducke</u> will <u>snap</u> at the <u>vet</u>.
       A   B   C

NONE
5. Ⓐ Ⓑ Ⓒ Ⓓ

6. <u>Hop</u> on the <u>wet</u> <u>ruge</u>.
    E   F   G

NONE
6. Ⓔ Ⓕ Ⓖ Ⓗ

Go on

7. The <u>hog</u> is <u>hot</u> in the <u>shedd</u>.
      A   B   C

NONE
7. Ⓐ Ⓑ Ⓒ Ⓓ

8. Go to the <u>vete</u> with the <u>wet</u> <u>cat</u>.
          E   F G

NONE
8. Ⓔ Ⓕ Ⓖ Ⓗ

9. You can <u>lok</u> him up, <u>but</u> not in the <u>shed</u>.
         A   B   C

NONE
9. Ⓐ Ⓑ Ⓒ Ⓓ

10. <u>Hop</u> on the <u>doll</u>, but do not <u>snape</u> it.
      E   F   G

NONE
10. Ⓔ Ⓕ Ⓖ Ⓗ

11. The <u>duck</u> can not <u>hoppe</u> on the <u>rug</u>.
       A   B   C

NONE
11. Ⓐ Ⓑ Ⓒ Ⓓ

12. Go to the <u>shed</u>, <u>buut</u> do not get <u>wet</u>.
        E   F   G

NONE
12. Ⓔ Ⓕ Ⓖ Ⓗ

13. The <u>cat</u> on the <u>rug</u> is <u>hotte</u>.
       A   B   C

NONE
13. Ⓐ Ⓑ Ⓒ Ⓓ

14. <u>Snap</u> the <u>lock</u> if it is <u>wet</u>.
      E   F   G

NONE
14. Ⓔ Ⓕ Ⓖ Ⓗ

15. He put the <u>catt</u> and the <u>hen</u> on a <u>rug</u>.
        A   B   C

NONE
15. Ⓐ Ⓑ Ⓒ Ⓓ

Words with Blends

Complete each word by writing the letters **mp**, **nt**, or **sp** on the line.

1. bu ____ **mp** ____   2. we _____

3. _____ ill   4. ju _____

5. te _____   6. _____ ell

Directions (to teacher)

Write the word *bump* on the chalkboard or form the word with letter cards. Say the word aloud and have children repeat it. Have them listen for the sounds /m/ and /p/ together at the end of the word. Then have them look at the first example. Point out that *mp* has been filled in.

Display the word *went*. Say the word and have children repeat it. Ask them to listen for the two sounds at the end of the word (/n/ and /t/). Have them complete the second example.

Display the word *spill* and repeat the process above, having students listen for the sounds at the beginning of the word (/s/ and /p/). Have them complete the third example.

Then display the words *jump*, *tent*, and *spell*. Say the words and have children repeat them. Have children listen for /mp/, /nt/, or /sp/ in each word. Then have them complete the page.

Book 1.3
Stan's Stunt

Name_____ Date_____

Words with Blends

Using the Word Study Steps

1. LOOK at the word.

2. SAY the word aloud.

3. STUDY the letters in the word.

4. WRITE the word.

5. CHECK the word.
   Did you spell the word right? If not,
   go back to step 1.

Spelling Tip

Rhyming words are often spelled alike. A word you know can help you spell a new word.

w + ent = went

t + ent = tent

Word Scramble

Unscramble each set of letters to make a spelling word.

1. mbup _____

2. nett _____

3. lpsil _____

4. tenw _____

5. pjmu _____

6. lpsel _____

To Parents or Helpers:

Using the Word Study Steps above as your child comes across any new words will help him or her spell well. Review the steps as you both go over this week's spelling words.

Go over the Spelling Tip with your child. Ask if he or she knows other words that rhyme with the spelling words. Help your child write new words that rhyme with the word he or she wants to spell.

Help your child complete the spelling activity.

Words with Blends

Look at the spelling words in the box.

tent bump spell jump spill went

Write the words that end with **mp**.

1. _____   2. _____

Write the words that end with **nt**.

3. _____   4. _____

Write the words that begin with **sp**.

5. _____   6. _____

Name_____ Date_____

Words with Blends

Look at the picture. Write two rhyming spelling
words to complete the sentences.

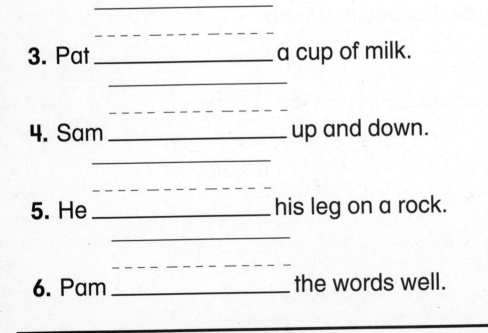

I. Dad and I _____
   camping.

2. We slept in a _____ .

Look at the spelling words in the box.

bump	jump	spill	spell

Write a spelling word to complete each sentence.
Add s to each word.

3. Pat _____ a cup of milk.

4. Sam _____ up and down.

5. He _____ his leg on a rock.

6. Pam _____ the words well.

Words with Blends

Look at the picture. Complete the sentence with a spelling word.

1. Did the cat _____ the milk?

2. We set up the _____.

3. How do you _____ that word?

4. Sally can _____ fast.

5. Do not _____ your head!

6. Write a sentence with the word went.

_____

_____

_____

Words with Blends

Look at the words in each set. One word in each set is spelled correctly. Use a pencil to color in the circle in front of that word. Before you begin, look at the sample sets of words. Sample A has been done for you. Do Sample B by yourself. When you are sure you know what to do, you may go on with the rest of the page.

Sample A
- (A) spot
- (B) spott
- (C) sopt

Sample B
- (D) snap
- (E) sanp
- (F) snapp

1. (A) sepll
   (B) spell
   (C) sopt

4. (D) tetn
   (E) tent
   (F) tennt

2. (D) went
   (E) wetn
   (F) whent

5. (A) spil
   (B) sipl
   (C) spill

3. (A) jupm
   (B) jummp
   (C) jump

6. (D) bummp
   (E) bump
   (F) bunp

Words with Blends

Complete each word by writing **cl**, **tr**, or **dr**
on the line.

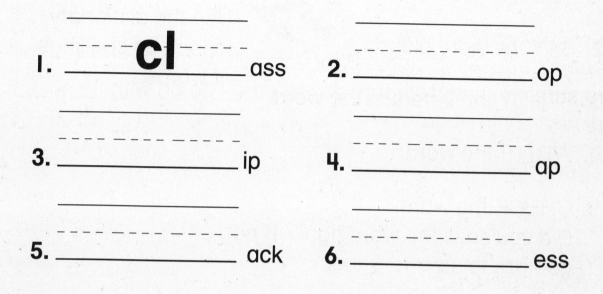

1. _____ **cl** _____ ass   2. _____ op

3. _____ ip   4. _____ ap

5. _____ ack   6. _____ ess

Directions (to teacher)

Write the word class on the chalkboard or form the word with letter cards.
Say the word aloud and have children repeat it. Have them listen for the
sounds /k/ and /l/ together at the beginning of the word. Then point out the
first example with cl filled in.

Display the word drop. Say the word and have children repeat it. Ask them
to listen for the two sounds at the beginning of the word (/d/ and /r/). Have
them complete the second example.

Display the word *trip* and repeat the process above, having students listen
for /t/ and /r/. Have them complete the third example.

Then display the words clap, track, and dress. Say the words and have
children repeat them. Have children listen for /cl/, /tr/, or /dr/ in each word.
Then have them complete the page.

Name_____ Date_____

Words with Blends

Using the Word Study Steps

1. LOOK at the word.

2. SAY the word aloud.

3. STUDY the letters in the word.

4. WRITE the word.

5. CHECK the word.
   Did you spell the word right? If not,
   go back to step 1.

Find and Circle

Where are the spelling words?

```
p  c  l  a  s  s  d  r  o  p  k
c  l  a  p  s  t  r  a  c  k  t
w  t  r  i  p  h  d  r  e  s  s
```

To Parents or Helpers:
   Using the Word Study Steps above as your child comes across any new words will help him or her spell well. Review the steps as you both go over this week's spelling words.
   Go over the Spelling Tip with your child. Help your child use the dictionary to look up spellings of words.
   Help your child find and circle the spelling words in the puzzle.

Words with Blends

Look at the spelling words in the box.

| track dress class drop clap trip |

Write the words that begin with **cl**.

1. _____   2. _____

Write the words that begin with **tr**.

3. _____   4. _____

Write the words that begin with **dr**.

5. _____   6. _____

Name_____ Date_____

Words with Blends

Write a spelling word from the box to match each picture. Add **s** to each spelling word.

drop	clap	track	trip

I. _____

2. _____

3. _____

4. _____

Write a spelling word from the box to match each picture. Add **es** to each spelling word.

dress	class

5. _____

6. _____

Words with Blends

Look at each picture. Use a spelling word to
complete each sentence.

1. The train runs on the _____ .

2. Mom has a new _____ .

3. My _____ put on a show.

4. Look at the people _____ !

5. Do not _____ the dish!

6. We went on a _____
in the car.

Words with Blends

Look at the words in each set. One word in each set is spelled correctly. Use a pencil to color in the circle in front of that word. Before you begin, look at the sample sets of words. Sample A has been done for you. Do Sample B by yourself. When you are sure you know what to do, you may go on with the rest of the page.

Sample A
- (A) drip
- (B) dripp
- (C) dirp

Sample B
- (D) tente
- (E) tenit
- (F) tent

1. (A) classe
   (B) clas
   (C) class

4. (D) dres
   (E) dress
   (F) driss

2. (D) dorp
   (E) drop
   (F) dropp

5. (A) clap
   (B) clapp
   (C) clape

3. (A) trakc
   (B) trac
   (C) track

6. (D) trpi
   (E) trip
   (F) tripp

Words with ch, wh, nk

1. ____**ch**____ in

2. _____ en

3. si _____

4. _____ ick

5. wi _____

6. thi _____

Directions (to teacher)

Review the digraph *ch* by explaining that the letters *ch* spell /ch/ as in the word *chin*. Write *chin* on the chalkboard or form the word with letter cards. Say the word aloud and have children repeat it. Have them listen for the sound /ch/ at the beginning of the word. Point out that *ch* has been filled in in the first example.

Display the word *when*. Say the word aloud and have children repeat it. Explain that the letters **wh** spell the sound /hw/. Have them listen for the sound /hw/ at the beginning of the word. Then have them complete the second example.

Display the word *sink*. Explain that the letters *nk* spell the sound /nk/ at the end of the word. Have children repeat the word and complete the third example.

Write the words *chick, wink,* and *think* on the chalkboard. Read the words aloud and have children repeat them. Then repeat each word and circle the letters that stand for the digraph *ch* at the beginning of the word or the digraph *nk* at the end of the word. Have children complete each word in the space provided.

Words with Digraphs *ch, wh, nk*

Using the Word Study Steps

1. LOOK at the word.

2. SAY the word aloud.

3. STUDY the letters in the word.

4. WRITE the word.

5. CHECK the word.
   Did you spell the word right? If not,
   go back to step 1.

<table>
<tr><td colspan="2">

Spelling Tip

Use beginnings and endings of words you can spell to help you spell new words.

thin + **s**ink = **think**
</td></tr>
</table>

X the Word

In each row, put an X on the word that does not belong.

1.	chin	thin	rack
2.	when	hat	then
3.	lake	stop	rake
4.	chick	lick	went
5.	sink	red	blue
6.	ran	think	pink

To Parents or Helpers:

Using the Word Study Steps above as your child comes across any new words will help him or her spell well. Review the steps as you both go over this week's spelling words.

Go over the Spelling Tip with your child. Help your child write new words that use beginnings and endings of words he or she can spell.

Help your child complete the spelling activity.

Name_____ Date_____

Words with *ch, wh, nk*

Look at the spelling words in the box.

| chin   when   wink   chick   sink   think |

Name the pictures. Listen for the beginning sound.
Write the spelling words that begin with the same sound.

1. _____

2. _____

3. _____

Name the picture. Listen for the ending sound. Write
the spelling words that end with the same sound.

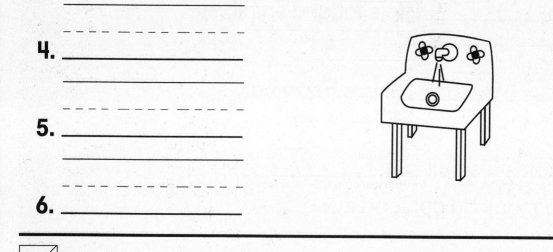

4. _____

5. _____

6. _____

Words with *ch, wh, nk*

Read these poems. Complete each spelling word
with the letters **ch**, **wh**, or **nk**.

_____   _____

- - - - - - - - - - - -   - - - - - - - - - -
_____ en the ship starts to si _____ ,

                                _____
                                - - - - - - - - - -
we go to help it, quick as a wi _____ .

_____
- - - - - - - - - -
A _____ ick is fat and small.

_____
- - - - - - - - - -
I thi _____ it is a fuzzy ball.

                            _____
                            - - - - - - - - - -
A chick has a small _____ in.

It has a mouth to put food in.

Words with ch, wh, nk

Look at each picture. Use a spelling word to complete each sentence.

_____

- - - - - - - - - - - - - -

1. That small new _____ is my pet.

_____

- - - - - - - - - - - - - -

2. You have a spot on your _____ .

_____

- - - - - - - - - - - - - -

3. Did she _____ at you?

4. We wash dishes in

_____

- - - - - - - - - - - - - -

the _____ .

Look at the picture. Use the spelling words in the box to complete the sentence.

when	think

_____

- - - - - - - - - - - - - -

Did the girl _____ ,

_____

- - - - - - - - - - - - - -

"_____ will we eat?"

Words with *ch*, *wh*, *th*

Look at the words in each set. One word in each set is spelled correctly. Use a pencil to color in the circle in front of that word. Before you begin, look at the sample sets of words. Sample A has been done for you. Do Sample B by yourself. When you are sure you know what to do, you may go on with the rest of the page.

Sample A

Ⓐ chop
Ⓑ hcop
Ⓒ chopp

Sample B

Ⓓ drope
Ⓔ drop
Ⓕ dorp

1. Ⓐ winc
   Ⓑ wink
   Ⓒ wikn

4. Ⓓ thinc
   Ⓔ thinke
   Ⓕ think

2. Ⓓ chin
   Ⓔ chinn
   Ⓕ chni

5. Ⓐ sink
   Ⓑ sinc
   Ⓒ sienk

3. Ⓐ wen
   Ⓑ wenn
   Ⓒ when

6. Ⓓ chik
   Ⓔ chikc
   Ⓕ chick

Words with Long a: a-e

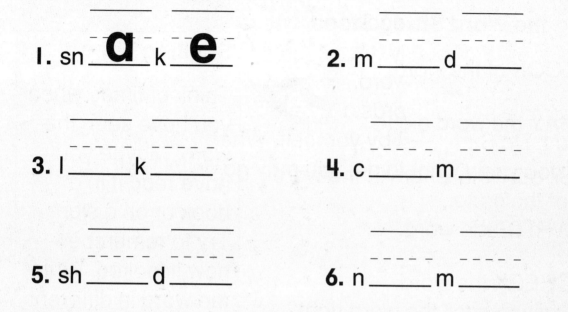

I. sn __ **a** __ k __ **e** __

2. m _____ d _____

3. l _____ k _____

4. c _____ m _____

5. sh _____ d _____

6. n _____ m _____

Directions (to teacher)

Review the long *a* sound by explaining the silent *e* rule. Present the CVCe (consonant-vowel-consonant-e) pattern as in *snake*. Write *snake* on the chalkboard or form the word with letter cards. Say the word aloud and have children repeat it. Then have them look at the first example on the page. Point out that the letter a and the silent e have been filled in.

Write the words *lake, made, came, shade,* and *name* on the chalkboard. Read the words aloud and have children repeat them. Then repeat each word and circle the letters that stand for the long *a* sound (*a* and silent *e*). Have children complete each word in the spaces provided.

Words with long *a: a-e*

Using the Word Study Steps

1. LOOK at the word.

2. SAY the word aloud.

3. STUDY the letters in the word.

4. WRITE the word.

5. CHECK the word.
   Did you spell the word right?
   If not, go back to step 1.

Spelling Tip

Think of times when you have seen the word. Maybe you have read it in a book or on a sign. Try to remember how it looked. Write the word in different ways to see which one looks correct.

~~lak~~ ~~lacke~~ lake

Fill in the Blank

Write the spelling word that best fits each sentence.

1. There is no sun in the _____.

2. She _____ to the park.

3. I saw a _____ at the zoo.

4. The _____ is blue.

5. I _____ a cake.

6. What is your _____?

To Parents or Helpers:
   Using the Word Study Steps above as your child comes across any new words will help him or her spell well. Review the steps as you both go over this week's spelling words.
   Go over the Spelling Tip with your child. Help your child write new words in different ways to see which one looks right.
   Help your child complete the spelling activity.

Words with Long *a* : *a-e*

Look at the spelling words in the box.

snake made lake came shade name

Find the spelling words in the snake. Circle each spelling word.

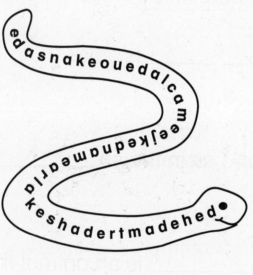

Write each spelling word under the correct snake.

Words with ending **ade**   Words with ending **ame**   Words with ending **ake**

1. _____   3. _____   5. _____

2. _____   4. _____   6. _____

Words with Long *a* : *a-e*

Read the sentences. Complete each spelling word
with **ade**, **ame**, or **ake**.

1. You can swim in a l _____ .

2. My n _____ is Jake.

3. When it is hot, I sit in the sh _____ .

4. A sn _____ is an animal that cannot run.

5. The baby snake c _____ out of its shell.

6. The snake m _____ a nest in the grass.

Name_____ Date_____

Words with Long *a* : *a-e*

Read the story. Use the spelling words to complete the story.

_____

My _____ is Sam. I am

a baby _____ . I

_____ out of a shell. I

used my egg tooth to get out.

My Mom and Dad swim in a

_____

_____ with the other

snakes.

When it is hot, they rest in

_____

the _____ of the tree.

They _____ a nest

for me in the grass. I like it there!

Words with Long *a* : a-e

Look at the words in each set. One word in each set is spelled correctly. Use a pencil to color in the circle in front of that word. Before you begin, look at the sample sets of words. Sample A has been done for you. Do Sample B by yourself. When you are sure you know what to do, you may go on with the rest of the page.

Sample A
- (A) make ●
- (B) mak
- (C) maek

Sample B
- (D) sikn
- (E) singk
- (F) sink

1. (A) nam
   (B) naem
   (C) name

2. (D) lak
   (E) lake
   (F) laek

3. (A) sanke
   (B) snak
   (C) snake

4. (D) made
   (E) maed
   (F) madde

5. (A) caem
   (B) came
   (C) camme

6. (D) shade
   (E) shede
   (F) shead

Words from Science

1. _Sticks_

2. _____

3. _____

4. _____

5. _____

6. _____

Directions (to teacher)

Write the words *sticks, sun, twigs, fire, snow,* and *mud* on the chalkboard. Have children find the word sticks filled in on this page. Read the word aloud and have them repeat it.

Tell children they will be writing the other five words on this page. Read each word aloud. Have children repeat it and write it in the blank provided.

You may also wish to present the challenge words *try, old, eat,* and *under.*

Words from Science

Using the Word Study Steps

1. LOOK at the word.

2. SAY the word aloud.

3. STUDY the letters in the word.

4. WRITE the word.

5. CHECK the word.
   Did you spell the word right? If not,
   go back to step 1.

Spelling Tip

Add -s to most words to tell about more than one.

stick + **s** = stick**s**
fire + **s** = fire**s**

Find and Circle

Where are the spelling words?

s	s	t	i	c	k	s	a	s	u	n
o	t	w	i	g	s	r	f	i	r	e
r	c	s	n	o	w	e	p	m	u	d

To Parents or Helpers:

Using the Word Study Steps above as your child comes across any new words will help him or her spell well. Review the steps as you both go over this week's spelling words.

Go over the Spelling Tip with your child. Help your child add -s to words to tell about more than one.

Help your child find and circle the spelling words in the puzzle.

Words from Science

Look at the spelling words in the box.

sticks sun twigs fire snow mud

Write each spelling word on the line where
it belongs.
Write the spelling words with three letters.

1. _____   2. _____

Write the spelling words with four letters.

3. _____   4. _____

Write the spelling word with five letters.

5. _____

Write the spelling word with six letters.

6. _____

Words from Science

Look at each picture. Complete each sentence with
a spelling word.

1. When the _____ is
out, it can be hot.

2. They make cakes out of

_____

_____just for fun.

3. We can make a man out

of _____.

4. A _____ can
make us warm.

Each spelling word below tells about more than one.
Rewrite each word so that it tells about only one.

5. sticks _____

6. twigs _____

Words from Science

Read the story. Use the spelling words to complete the story.

We like to hike when the

_____

_____

_____ is hot.

When it is wet, we sink into

_____

_____

the _____ .We carry

_____

_____

big _____ so we will

not fall.

We even hike when there

_____

_____

is _____ on the

ground. We get lots of

_____

_____

_____ from trees

_____

_____

to make a _____ .

Then it is hot!

Name_____ Date_____

Words from Science

Look at the words in each set. One word in each set is spelled correctly. Use a pencil to color in the circle in front of that word. Before you begin, look at the sample sets of words. Sample A has been done for you. Do Sample B by yourself. When you are sure you know what to do, you may go on with the rest of the page.

Sample A
- (A) think
- (B) tink
- (C) thingk

Sample B
- (D) came
- (E) cam
- (F) camme

I. (A) stics
   (B) stiks
   (C) sticks

4. (D) fier
   (E) fire
   (F) frire

2. (D) muhd
   (E) mudd
   (F) mud

5. (A) tigs
   (B) twigs
   (C) twigz

3. (A) snow
   (B) sno
   (C) snoe

6. (D) sun
   (E) sunn
   (F) sunne

Book 1.3 Unit Review Test

Read each sentence. If an underlined word is spelled wrong, fill in the circle that goes with that word. If no word is spelled wrong, fill in the circle below NONE.

Read Sample A, and do Sample B.

A. The <u>ducke</u> <u>can</u> <u>quack</u>.
    A   B   C

NONE
A. Ⓐ Ⓑ Ⓒ Ⓓ

B. It was <u>hot</u> and <u>wett</u> in the <u>shed</u>.
           E   F   G

NONE
B. Ⓔ Ⓕ Ⓖ Ⓗ

I. <u>Drop</u> the <u>tent</u> in the <u>shadde</u>.
     A   B   C

NONE
I. Ⓐ Ⓑ Ⓒ Ⓓ

2. On the <u>trip</u> I got a <u>bummp</u> on my <u>chin</u>.
            E   F   G

NONE
2. Ⓔ Ⓕ Ⓖ Ⓗ

3. <u>Wen</u> did you <u>drop</u> the <u>twigs</u>?
     A   B   C

NONE
3. Ⓐ Ⓑ Ⓒ Ⓓ

4. I <u>thinnk</u> she <u>came</u> to the <u>tent</u>.
       E   F   G

NONE
4. Ⓔ Ⓕ Ⓖ Ⓗ

5. The <u>class</u> <u>trip</u> is in the <u>sunn</u>.
         A   B   C

NONE
5. Ⓐ Ⓑ Ⓒ Ⓓ

6. Did you <u>spille</u> <u>snow</u> in the <u>tent</u>?
             E   F   G

NONE
6. Ⓔ Ⓕ Ⓖ Ⓗ

Go on →

7. Do not <u>drope</u> the <u>snake</u> in the <u>tent</u>.
    A   B   C

7. Ⓐ Ⓑ Ⓒ Ⓓ

8. The <u>sno</u> will <u>drop</u> on my <u>chin</u>.
    E   F   G

8. Ⓔ Ⓕ Ⓖ Ⓗ

9. I hurt my <u>chinn</u> on a <u>class</u> <u>trip</u>.
         A   B   C

9. Ⓐ Ⓑ Ⓒ Ⓓ

10. I <u>think</u> there is a <u>snaake</u> in the <u>snow</u>.
       E   F   G

10. Ⓔ Ⓕ Ⓖ Ⓗ

11. The <u>class</u> <u>came</u> on the <u>trip</u>.
         A   B   C

11. Ⓐ Ⓑ Ⓒ Ⓓ

12. <u>Drop</u> the <u>twegs</u> in the <u>snow</u>.
       E   F   G

12. Ⓔ Ⓕ Ⓖ Ⓗ

13. On our <u>tripp</u> we had <u>sun</u> and <u>snow</u>.
            A   B   C

13. Ⓐ Ⓑ Ⓒ Ⓓ

14. I <u>think</u> the <u>tente</u> is in the <u>sun</u>.
       E   F   G

14. Ⓔ Ⓕ Ⓖ Ⓗ

15. Did the <u>classe</u> <u>spill</u> the <u>twigs</u>?
             A   B   C

15. Ⓐ Ⓑ Ⓒ Ⓓ

Name_____ Date_____ PRETEST **SPELLING** **97**

Words with Long i : i-e

Pretest Directions

Fold back the paper along the dotted line. Use the blanks to write each word as it is read aloud. When you finish the test, unfold the paper. Use the list at the right to correct any spelling mistakes. Practice the words you missed for the Posttest.

1. _____   1. smile

2. _____   2. white

3. _____   3. wide

4. _____   4. while

5. _____   5. bite

6. _____   6. hide

Challenge Words

_____   after

_____   blue

_____   were

_____   who

To Parents

Here are the results of your child's weekly spelling Pretest. You can help your child study for the Posttest by following these simple steps for each word on the list:

1. Read the word to your child.

2. Have your child write the word, saying each letter as it is written.

3. Say each letter of the word as your child checks the spelling.

4. If a mistake has been made, have your child read each letter of the correctly spelled word aloud, and then repeat steps 1-3.

Words with Long *i*: *i-e*

Using the Word Study Steps

1. LOOK at the word.

2. SAY the word aloud.

3. STUDY the letters in the word.

4. WRITE the word.

5. CHECK the word.
   Did you spell the word right?
   If not, go back to step 1.

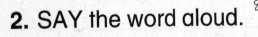

Spelling Tip

When there is a long vowel sound at the beginning or in the middle of a one-syllable word, it usually has two vowels.

wide

X the Word

In each row, put an X on the word that does not belong.

1.	smile	pile	win
2.	white	pan	red
3.	wide	dig	tide
4.	hot	cold	while
5.	bite	back	kite
6.	lake	hide	ride

To Parents or Helpers:

Using the Word Study Steps above as your child comes across any new words will help him or her spell well. Review the steps as you both go over this week's spelling words.

Go over the Spelling Tip with your child. Help your child write new one-syllable words that have a long vowel sound at the beginning or in the middle and have two vowels.

Help your child complete the spelling activity.

Name_____ Date_____

Words with Long i : i-e

Look at the spelling words in the box.

smile   white   wide   while   bite   hide

Write the two letters that are found in
every spelling word.

1. _____   2. _____

Write the words that end with **ite.**

3. _____   4. _____

Write the words that end with **ile.**

5. _____   6. _____

Write the words that end with **ide.**

7. _____   8. _____

Words with Long i : i-e

Look at the pictures. Complete each spelling word by adding **ite**, **ile**, or **ide**.

1. My pal Dina always has a big

sm _____ on her face.

2. Her teeth are wh _____ .

3. Her grin is very w _____ .

4. The dog will not

b _____ your hand.

5. He will wag his tail wh _____ you pet him.

6. Sometimes he likes to

h _____ in his doghouse.

Words with Long i : i-e

Finding Mistakes
Read the poem. There are six spelling mistakes.
Circle the mistakes. Write the words correctly on
the lines.

A tent that is whide

Is a good place to hyd.

All the whyle,

I sit and smil.

I take a bitte

Of cake so wite.

1. _____

2. _____

3. _____

4. _____

5. _____

6. _____

Write a sentence using two words you wrote.

_____

_____

_____

Words with Long i : i-e

Look at the words in each set. One word in each set is spelled correctly. Use a pencil to color in the circle in front of that word. Before you begin, look at the sample sets of words. Sample A has been done for you. Do Sample B by yourself. When you are sure you know what to do, you may go on with the rest of the page.

Sample A
- (A) side ●
- (B) sid
- (C) sidde

Sample B
- (D) lak
- (E) lacke
- (F) lake

1.
- (A) byt
- (B) biet
- (C) bite

4.
- (D) hyde
- (E) heid
- (F) hide

2.
- (D) while
- (E) wile
- (F) whyl

5.
- (A) smyl
- (B) smile
- (C) smil

3.
- (A) wid
- (B) wide
- (C) wyde

6.
- (D) wite
- (E) white
- (F) whyte

Words with Long o: o-e

Pretest Directions

Fold back the paper along the dotted line. Use the blanks to write each word as it is read aloud. When you finish the test, unfold the paper. Use the list at the right to correct any spelling mistakes. Practice the words you missed for the Posttest.

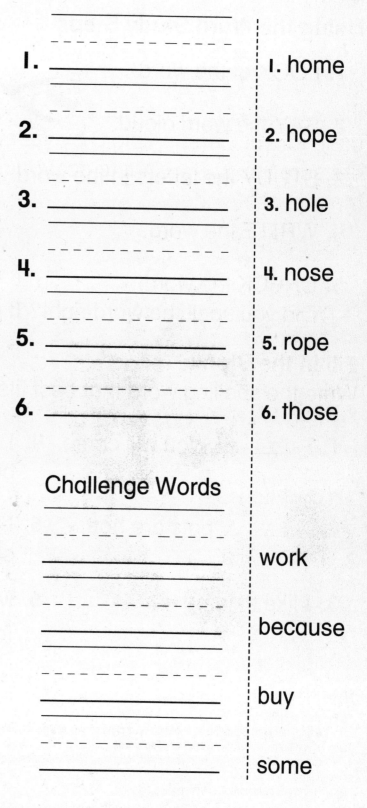

1. _____   1. home

2. _____   2. hope

3. _____   3. hole

4. _____   4. nose

5. _____   5. rope

6. _____   6. those

Challenge Words

_____ work

_____ because

_____ buy

_____ some

To Parents

Here are the results of your child's weekly spelling Pretest. You can help your child study for the Posttest by following these simple steps for each word on the list:

1. Read the word to your child.

2. Have your child write the word, saying each letter as it is written.

3. Say each letter of the word as your child checks the spelling.

4. If a mistake has been made, have your child read each letter of the correctly spelled word aloud, and then repeat steps 1-3.

Words with Long *o* : *o-e*

Using the Word Study Steps

1. LOOK at the word.

2. SAY the word aloud.

3. STUDY the letters in the word.

4. WRITE the word.

5. CHECK the word.
Did you spell the word right? If not, go back to step 1.

Spelling Tip

Use beginnings and endings of words you can spell to help you spell new words.

then + n**ose** = **those**

Fill in the Blank

Write the spelling word that best fits each sentence.

1. I _____ you will come.

2. _____ pots are hot!

3. I like to jump _____ .

4. I go _____ on the bus.

5. I have a _____ in my sock.

6. My _____ is on my face.

To Parents or Helpers:
    Using the Word Study Steps above as your child comes across any new words will help him or her spell well. Review the steps as you both go over this week's spelling words.
    Go over the Spelling Tip with your child. Help your child write new words that use beginnings and endings of words he or she can spell.
    Help your child complete the spelling activity.

Words with Long o: o-e

Look at the spelling words in the box.

| home | hope | hole | nose | rope | those |

Write the words that end with **ope.**

1. _____   2. _____

Write the words that end with **ose.**

3. _____   4. _____

Write the word that ends with **ome.**

5. _____

Write the word that ends with **ole.**

6. _____

All of these words have an **o** and a final **e.**

7. Which letter says its name? _____

8. Which letter is silent? _____

Words with Long o: o-e

Look at the pictures. Write the spelling word to answer each question.

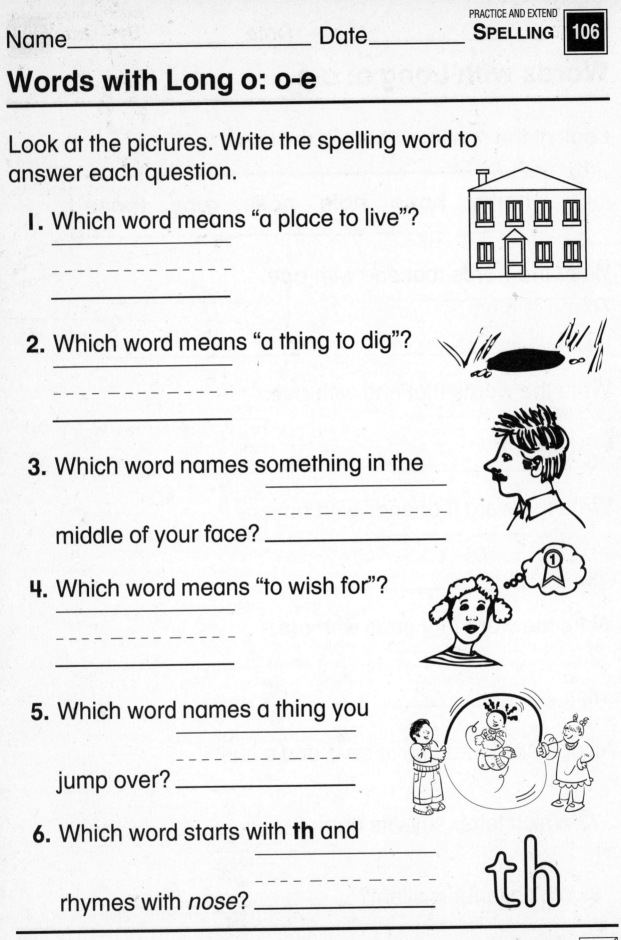

1. Which word means "a place to live"?
   _____
   - - - - - - - - - - -
   _____

2. Which word means "a thing to dig"?
   _____
   - - - - - - - - - - -
   _____

3. Which word names something in the
   _____
   - - - - - - - - - -
   middle of your face? _____

4. Which word means "to wish for"?
   _____
   - - - - - - - - - - -
   _____

5. Which word names a thing you
   _____
   - - - - - - - - -
   jump over? _____

6. Which word starts with **th** and
   _____
   - - - - - - - - -
   rhymes with *nose*? _____

Words with Long o: o-e

Read the poem. There are six spelling mistakes.
Circle the mistakes. Write the words correctly on the lines.

Look at that hol.

It is hom to a mouse.

He packs it with roep.

To make a house.

He adds thin sticks.

Can you see thoze?

I hopp we see him.

Look! There is his noze.

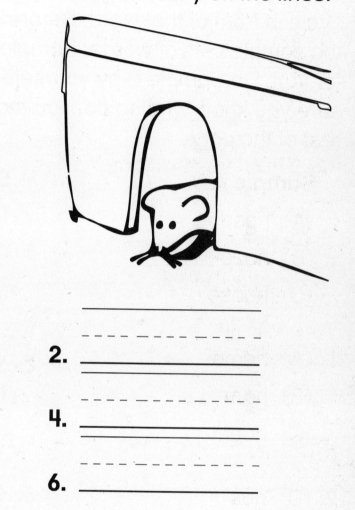

1. _____

2. _____

3. _____

4. _____

5. _____

6. _____

Writing Activity
Write a story telling about an animal you like.
Use three spelling words in your story.

_____

_____

_____

Words with Long o: o-e

Look at the words in each set. One word in each set is spelled correctly. Use a pencil to color in the circle in front of that word. Before you begin, look at the sample sets of words. Sample A has been done for you. Do Sample B by yourself. When you are sure you know what to do, you may go on with the rest of the page.

Sample A
- (A) hose
- (B) hoze
- (C) hoose

Sample B
- (D) bitte
- (E) bite
- (F) byt

1. (A) home
   (B) hom
   (C) hoem

4. (D) hopp
   (E) hope
   (F) hoope

2. (D) nos
   (E) nose
   (F) noze

5. (A) rope
   (B) rop
   (C) roope

3. (A) whol
   (B) hol
   (C) hole

6. (D) thoz
   (E) those
   (F) thos

Words with Long u: u-e

Pretest Directions

Fold back the paper along the dotted line. Use the blanks to write each word as it is read aloud. When you finish the test, unfold the paper. Use the list at the right to correct any spelling mistakes. Practice the words you missed for the Posttest.

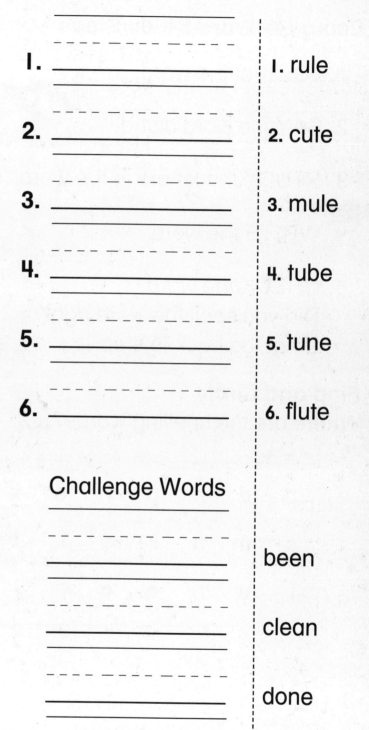

1. _____ 1. rule

2. _____ 2. cute

3. _____ 3. mule

4. _____ 4. tube

5. _____ 5. tune

6. _____ 6. flute

Challenge Words

_____ been

_____ clean

_____ done

_____ far

To Parents

Here are the results of your child's weekly spelling Pretest. You can help your child study for the Posttest by following these simple steps for each word on the list:

1. Read the word to your child.

2. Have your child write the word, saying each letter as it is written.

3. Say each letter of the word as your child checks the spelling.

4. If a mistake has been made, have your child read each letter of the correctly spelled word aloud, and then repeat steps 1-3.

Words with Long *u* : *u-e*

Using the Word Study Steps

1. LOOK at the word.

2. SAY the word aloud.

3. STUDY the letters in the word.

4. WRITE the word.

5. CHECK the word.
   Did you spell the word right?
   If not, go back to step 1.

Spelling Tip

When there is a long vowel sound at the beginning or in the middle of a one-syllable word, it usually has two vowels.

tune   flute

Find and Circle
Where are the spelling words?

p	d	r	u	l	e	k	c	u	t	e
s	m	u	l	e	i	t	u	b	e	o
t	u	n	e	q	f	l	u	t	e	g

To Parents or Helpers:
    Using the Word Study Steps above as your child comes across any new words will help him or her spell well. Review the steps as you both go over this week's spelling words.
    Go over the Spelling Tip with your child. Help your child write new one-syllable words that have a long vowel sound at the beginning or in the middle and have two vowels.
    Help your child find and circle the spelling words in the puzzle.

Words with Long u: u-e

Look at the spelling words in the box.

rule cute mule tube tune flute

Write the words that end with **ule**.

1._____ 2._____

Write the words that end with **ute**.

3._____ 4._____

Write the word that ends with **une**.

5._____

Write the two letters that are found in every spelling word.

6._____ 7._____

Make a new word by changing the **r** of **rule** to **m**.

8._____

Words with Long u: u-e

Look at the pictures. Complete each spelling word.

1. You can ride on a m _____ .

2. Another word for song is t _____ .

3. You can swim with a t _____ .

4. The baby pig is very c _____ .

5. You can play a fl _____ .

6. What you can or cannot

do is a r _____ .

Words with Long u: u-e

Finding Mistakes
Read the story. There are six spelling mistakes.
Circle the mistakes. Write the words correctly on the lines.

In June, Will and I go to a camp in the woods. We
ride on muls up and down the hills. We swim in the
lake with toobs. We learn to play a toon on a flut.
We take care of kute hens, chicks, and ducks. We
obey all the rools. We want to go back soon.

1. _____   2. _____   3. _____

4. _____   5. _____   6. _____

Writing Activity
Your school has rules. Write about a rule in your
school. Tell why it is a good rule.
Use two spelling words in your story.

_____
_____
_____
_____

Words with Long u: u-e

Look at the words in each set. One word in each set is spelled correctly. Use a pencil to color in the circle in front of that word. Before you begin, look at the sample sets of words. Sample A has been done for you. Do Sample B by yourself. When you are sure you know what to do, you may go on with the rest of the page.

Sample A

(A) rose

(B) ros

(C) roze

Sample B

(D) noze

(E) nos

(F) nose

1. (A) rool

   (B) rulle

   (C) rule

4. (D) kute

   (E) coote

   (F) cute

2. (D) flute

   (E) floote

   (F) flut

5. (A) toon

   (B) tune

   (C) tun

3. (A) mul

   (B) mule

   (C) myul

6. (D) tube

   (E) tubb

   (F) tobe

Words with Long a: ai, ay

Pretest Directions

Fold back the paper along the dotted line. Use the blanks to write each word as it is read aloud. When you finish the test, unfold the paper. Use the list at the right to correct any spelling mistakes. Practice the words you missed for the Posttest.

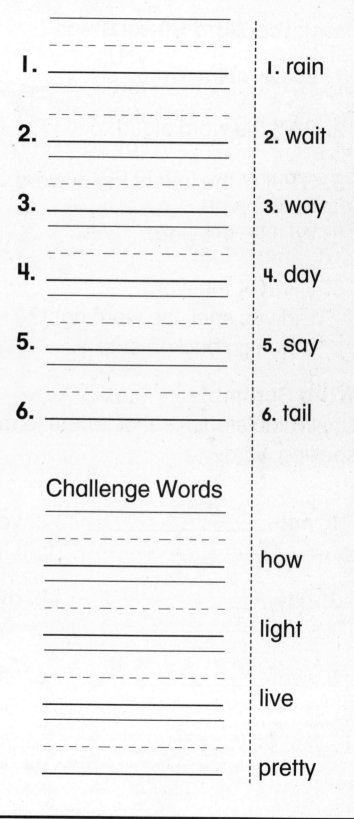

1. _____ 1. rain

2. _____ 2. wait

3. _____ 3. way

4. _____ 4. day

5. _____ 5. say

6. _____ 6. tail

Challenge Words

_____ how

_____ light

_____ live

_____ pretty

To Parents

Here are the results of your child's weekly spelling Pretest. You can help your child study for the Posttest by following these simple steps for each word on the list:

1. Read the word to your child.

2. Have your child write the word, saying each letter as it is written.

3. Say each letter of the word as your child checks the spelling.

4. If a mistake has been made, have your child read each letter of the correctly spelled word aloud, and then repeat steps 1-3.

Words with Long *a : ai, ay*

Using the Word Study Steps

I. LOOK at the word.

2. SAY the word aloud.

3. STUDY the letters in the word.

4. WRITE the word.

5. CHECK the word.
Did you spell the word right?
If not, go back to step I.

Spelling Tip

When there is a long vowel sound at the beginning or in the middle of a one-syllable word, it usually has two vowels.

ra**i**n   **s**a**y**

Word Scramble

Unscramble each set of letters to make a spelling word.

I. nria _____

2. yas _____

3. ady _____

4. ayw _____

5. iwat _____

6. ilta _____

To Parents or Helpers:
Using the Word Study Steps above as your child comes across any new words will help him or her spell well. Review the steps as you both go over this week's spelling words.
Go over the Spelling Tip with your child. Help your child write new one-syllable words that have a long vowel sound at the beginning or in the middle and have two vowels.
Help your child complete the spelling activity.

Words with Long a : ai, ay

Read the words. Circle the letters that are the same in each set of words.

1. rain   tail   wait

2. day   say   way

Write the letters that complete each spelling word.

3. r_____n   **4.** w_____t

5. w_____   **6.** d_____

7. s_____   **8.** t_____l

Read the rhyme. Circle the words that have the long **a** sound as in **may.**

I wait in the rain on a school day,

Hoping the bus will come my way.

Write the words you circled that have the long **a** spelled **ay.**

9. _____   **10.** _____

Write the words you circled that have the long **a** spelled **ai.**

11. _____   **12.** _____

Words with Long a : ai, ay

Complete each spelling word by adding letters that spell the long **a** sound as in **way.**

1. The r _____ n makes plants and grass grow.

2. D _____ is the opposite of night.

3. The dog wags her t _____ l when she is happy.

4. We w _____ t for the school bus together.

5. We s _____ "Hi!" to all our friends.

6. Then the bus goes on its w _____ .

Words with Long a: ai, ay

Read the poem. There are five spelling mistakes.
Circle the mistakes. Write the words correctly on
the lines.

Johnny Appleseed spent each dae

Giving apple seeds away.

"Plant these seeds," he would sai.

"And apple trees will line your wey.

Plant these seeds, Jack and Jane,

And then just wate for the raine."

1. _____ 2. _____

3. _____ 4. _____

5. _____

Johnny planted apples. What would you plant? Write a
poem or story. Use three spelling words.

_____

_____

_____

Words with Long a: ai, ay

Look at the words in each set. One word in each set is spelled correctly. Use a pencil to color in the circle in front of that word. Before you begin, look at the sample sets of words. Sample A has been done for you. Do Sample B by yourself. When you are sure you know what to do, you may go on with the rest of the page.

Sample A

(A) nail

(B) nale

(C) nayl

Sample B

(D) rool

(E) rule

(F) roul

1. (A) say

(B) sae

(C) saye

4. (D) dae

(E) daye

(F) day

2. (D) wate

(E) wayt

(F) wait

5. (A) raine

(B) rain

(C) rayn

3. (A) way

(B) waye

(C) wae

6. (D) tayl

(E) tail

(F) taile

Words from Science

Pretest Directions

Fold back the paper along the dotted line. Use the blanks to write each word as it is read aloud. When you finish the test, unfold the paper. Use the list at the right to correct any spelling mistakes. Practice the words you missed for the Posttest.

1. _____   1. truck

2. _____   2. smoke

3. _____   3. bell

4. _____   4. pole

5. _____   5. ring

6. _____   6. brave

Challenge Words

_____

_____   clean

_____   always

_____   work

_____   done

To Parents

Here are the results of your child's weekly spelling Pretest. You can help your child study for the Posttest by following these simple steps for each word on the list:

1. Read the word to your child.

2. Have your child write the word, saying each letter as it is written.

3. Say each letter of the word as your child checks the spelling.

4. If a mistake has been made, have your child read each letter of the correctly spelled word aloud, and then repeat steps 1-3.

Words from Social Studies

Using the Word Study Steps

1. LOOK at the word.

2. SAY the word aloud.

3. STUDY the letters in the word.

4. WRITE the word.

5. CHECK the word.
Did you spell the word right?
If not, go back to step 1.

Find and Circle
Where are the spelling words?

```
t  r  u  c  k  u  s  m  o  k  e

o  b  e  l  l  b  r  p  o  l  e

r  r  i  n  g  h  b  r  a  v  e
```

To Parents or Helpers:
 Using the Word Study Steps above as your child comes across any new words will help him or her spell well. Review the steps as you both go over this week's spelling words.
 Go over the Spelling Tip with your child. Help your child write words that they have trouble spelling in a notebook that they can keep.
 Help your child find and circle the spelling words in the puzzle.

122

Book 1. 4
Ring! Ring! Ring!
Put Out the Fire
6

Words from Social Studies

Look at the spelling words in the box. Write each word in the correct helmet.

| truck | smoke | bell | pole | ring | brave |

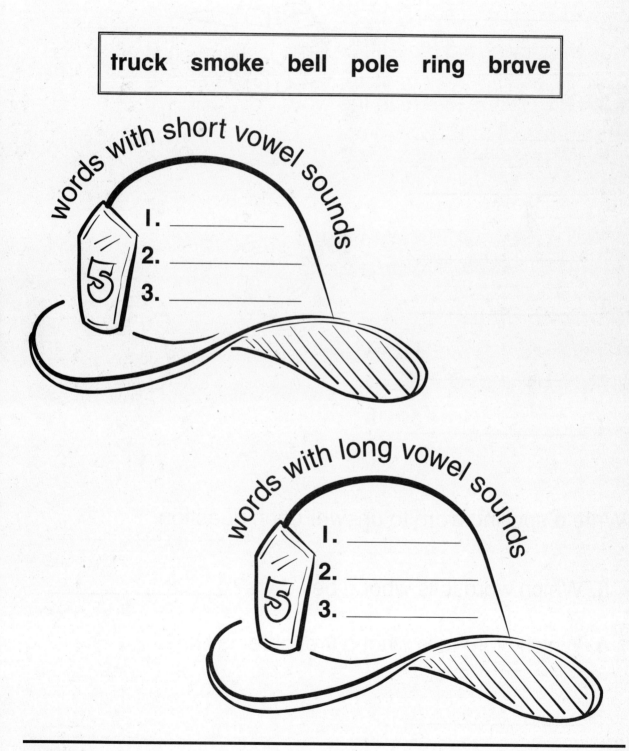

words with short vowel sounds

1. _____
2. _____
3. _____

words with long vowel sounds

1. _____
2. _____
3. _____

Words from Social Studies

Write the spelling word that goes with
each picture.

1. _____

2. _____

3. _____

4. _____

Write a spelling word to answer each question.

_____

5. Which word tells what a bell does? _____

6. Which word tells what a firefighter is like?

_____

Words from Social Studies

Finding Mistakes
Read the story. There are six spelling mistakes.
Circle the mistakes. Write the words correctly on
the lines.

The fire bel goes "Ringe!" The firefighters slide

down the pol. They jump into the fire truc. They

rush to put out a fire. They get there very fast.

When they see smok, they rush in to help.

Firefighters are very braav.

1. _____   2. _____   3. _____

4. _____   5. _____   6. _____

Writing Activity
Write a story about someone who was brave.
Use two spelling words in your story.

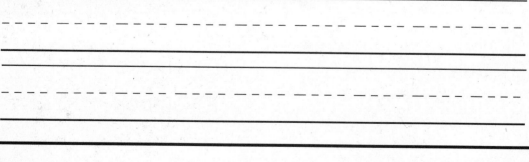

Words from Social Studies

Look at the words in each set. One word in each set is spelled correctly. Use a pencil to color in the circle in front of that word. Before you begin, look at the sample sets of words. Sample A has been done for you. Do Sample B by yourself. When you are sure you know what to do, you may go on with the rest of the page.

Sample A

(A) those

(B) thoze

(C) thos

Sample B

(D) wai

(E) wae

(F) way

1. (A) ringe

(B) rin

(C) ring

4. (D) poole

(E) pol

(F) pole

2. (D) braf

(E) brave

(F) brav

5. (A) bell

(B) bel

(C) bbel

3. (A) truc

(B) truk

(C) truck

6. (D) smok

(E) smoke

(F) smook

Book 1.4 Unit Review Test

Read each sentence. If an underlined word is spelled wrong, fill in the circle that goes with that word. If no word is spelled wrong, fill in the circle below NONE.

Read Sample A, and do Sample B.

A. The <u>twigs</u> will <u>drope</u> in the <u>snow</u>.
        A   B   C

                                                 NONE
A. Ⓐ **Ⓑ** Ⓒ Ⓓ

B. <u>When</u> was the <u>class</u> <u>tripe</u>?
      E   F   G

                                                 NONE
B. Ⓔ Ⓕ Ⓖ Ⓗ

1. That dog has a <u>white</u> <u>nose</u> and <u>taile</u>.
                    A   B   C

                                                 NONE
1. Ⓐ Ⓑ Ⓒ Ⓓ

2. I <u>hope</u> to fill the <u>tuube</u> with <u>white</u> seeds.
      E   F   G

                                                 NONE
2. Ⓔ Ⓕ Ⓖ Ⓗ

3. The baby at <u>home</u> has a cute <u>pink</u> <u>noize</u>.
                    A   B   C

                                               NONE
3. Ⓐ Ⓑ Ⓒ Ⓓ

4. Do not <u>hide</u> your <u>smyle</u> in the <u>smoke</u>.
             E   F   G

                                               NONE
4. Ⓔ Ⓕ Ⓖ Ⓗ

5. I <u>hope</u> it will not <u>raine</u> on that <u>day</u>.
      A   B   C

                                               NONE
5. Ⓐ Ⓑ Ⓒ Ⓓ

6. He will <u>hope</u> to find a <u>ring</u> at <u>hom</u>.
            E   F   G

                                              NONE
6. Ⓔ Ⓕ Ⓖ Ⓗ

Go on

7. <u>Hyde</u> from the <u>smoke</u> in the <u>tube</u>.
   A   B   C

NONE
7. Ⓐ Ⓑ Ⓒ Ⓓ

8. I <u>hope</u> to see a <u>whyte</u> <u>truck</u>.
   E   F   G

NONE
8. Ⓔ Ⓕ Ⓖ Ⓗ

9. The <u>smocke</u> came out of the <u>tube</u> in a <u>ring</u>.
   A   B   C

NONE
9. Ⓐ Ⓑ Ⓒ Ⓓ

10. One <u>daye</u> I will see the <u>truck</u> and <u>smile</u>.
    E   F   G

NONE
10. Ⓔ Ⓕ Ⓖ Ⓗ

11. We <u>hoppe</u> to know the <u>rule</u> of <u>day</u>.
    A   B   C

NONE
11. Ⓐ Ⓑ Ⓒ Ⓓ

12. I took the <u>white</u> <u>truk</u> <u>home</u>.
         E   F   G

NONE
12. Ⓔ Ⓕ Ⓖ Ⓗ

13. I will <u>hide</u> the <u>cute</u> <u>ringe</u>.
      A   B   C

NONE
13. Ⓐ Ⓑ Ⓒ Ⓓ

14. The <u>rulle</u> of the <u>day</u> is to <u>smile</u>.
    E   F   G

NONE
14. Ⓔ Ⓕ Ⓖ Ⓗ

15. She has a <u>cuut</u> <u>tail</u> and a small <u>nose</u>.
     A B   C

NONE
15. Ⓐ Ⓑ Ⓒ Ⓓ

Words with Long e : e, ee

Pretest Directions

Fold back the paper along the dotted line. Use the blanks to write each word as it is read aloud. When you finish the test, unfold the paper. Use the list at the right to correct any spelling mistakes. Practice the words you missed for the Posttest.

1. _____
2. _____
3. _____
4. _____
5. _____
6. _____

1. sheep
2. three
3. we
4. tree
5. she
6. bee

Challenge Words

_____ all

_____ four

_____ many

_____ over

To Parents

Here are the results of your child's weekly spelling Pretest. You can help your child study for the Posttest by following these simple steps for each word on the list:

1. Read the word to your child.

2. Have your child write the word, saying each letter as it is written.

3. Say each letter of the word as your child checks the spelling.

4. If a mistake has been made, have your child read each letter of the correctly spelled word aloud, and then repeat steps 1-3.

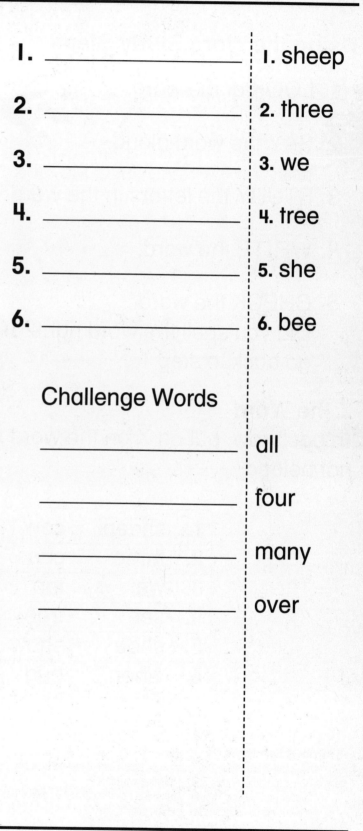

Words with Long *e* : *ee, e*

Using the Word Study Steps

1. LOOK at the word.

2. SAY the word aloud.

3. STUDY the letters in the word.

4. WRITE the word.

5. CHECK the word.
   Did you spell the word right? If not,
   go back to step 1.

Spelling Tip

Learn about sound-alike words like **be** and **bee.** Be sure you use the right word when you write something.

X the Word

In each row, put an X on the word that does not belong.

1.	sheep	cow	book
2.	three	can	four
3.	we	tap	he
4.	see	tree	go
5.	shoe	show	tent
6.	when	bug	bee

To Parents or Helpers:
Using the Word Study Steps above as your child comes across any new words will help him or her spell well. Review the steps as you both go over this week's spelling words.
Go over the Spelling Tip with your child. Ask if he or she knows other sound-alike words.
Help your child complete the spelling activity.

Words with Long e : e , ee

Look at the spelling words in the box.

sheep bee she three tree we

Write the spelling words that have long **e** spelled **e**.

1. _____ 2. _____

Write the spelling words that have long **e** spelled **ee**.

3. _____ 4. _____

5. _____ 6. _____

Write the missing letter or letters in each spelling word.

7. tr _____ 8. w _____

9. sh _____ p 10. thr _____

Words with Long e : e , ee

Look at the picture. Write a spelling word to complete the sentence.

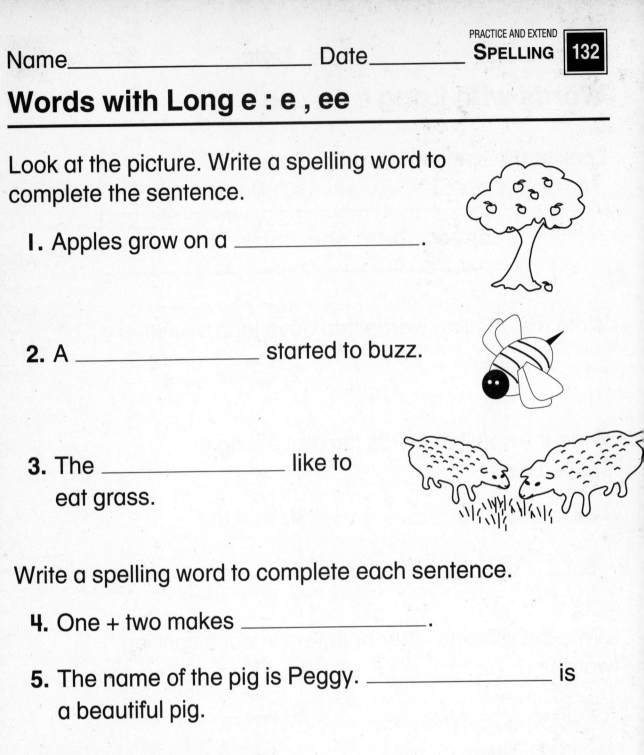

1. Apples grow on a _____.

2. A _____ started to buzz.

3. The _____ like to eat grass.

Write a spelling word to complete each sentence.

4. One + two makes _____.

5. The name of the pig is Peggy. _____ is a beautiful pig.

6. Don and I are friends. _____ are best friends.

Words with Long e : e , ee

Finding Mistakes
Read the story. There are six spelling mistakes. Circle the mistakes. Write the six words correctly on the lines.

It is a hot day. A shepe is eating
grass at the pond. Wee are at the
pond, too. There are thre of
us—me, my brother Matt, and my
sister Ann. Ann is sitting under a tre .
Then Ann jumps up and runs. A be is
buzzing around her. Shee jumps into the
pond. The bee goes away.

1. _____   2. _____

3. _____   4. _____

5. _____   6. _____

Writing Activity
Write more about Stan, Matt, and Ann. What happens next? Use two spelling words in your story.

_____

_____

Words with Long e : e, ee

Look at the words in each set. One word in each set is spelled correctly. Use a pencil to color in the circle in front of that word. Before you begin, look at the sample sets of words. Sample A has been done for you. Do Sample B by yourself. When you are sure you know what to do, you may go on with the rest of the page.

Sample A

(A) see
(B) se
(C) sse

Sample B

(D) tael
(E) tail
(F) tayl

1. (A) we
   (B) whe
   (C) wi

2. (D) thre
   (E) three
   (F) tre

3. (A) shep
   (B) sheep
   (C) seehp

4. (D) bee
   (E) bie
   (F) bea

5. (A) shea
   (B) shee
   (C) she

6. (D) treh
   (E) tre
   (F) tree

Words with Long e: ea, ie

Pretest Directions

Fold back the paper along the dotted line. Use the blanks to write each word as it is read aloud. When you finish the test, unfold the paper. Use the list at the right to correct any spelling mistakes. Practice the words you missed for the Posttest.

1. _____
2. _____
3. _____
4. _____
5. _____
6. _____

1. reached
2. fields
3. read
4. sea
5. piece
6. leaf

Challenge Words

_____
_____
_____
_____

before
off
our
come

To Parents

Here are the results of your child's weekly spelling Pretest. You can help your child study for the Posttest by following these simple steps for each word on the list:

1. Read the word to your child.

2. Have your child write the word, saying each letter as it is written.

3. Say each letter of the word as your child checks the spelling.

4. If a mistake has been made, have your child read each letter of the correctly spelled word aloud, and then repeat steps 1-3.

Words with Long *e* : *ea*, *ie*

Using the Word Study Steps

1. LOOK at the word.

2. SAY the word aloud.

3. STUDY the letters in the word.

4. WRITE the word.

5. CHECK the word.
   Did you spell the word right?
   If not, go back to step 1.

Spelling Tip

Add -ed to most words to tell about something in the past. Which spelling word tells about something that happened in the past?

reach + **ed** =reach**ed**

Find and Circle
Where are the spelling words?

s	e	a	a	r	e	a	c	h	e	d
f	i	e	l	d	s	c	r	e	a	d
p	i	e	c	e	c	l	e	a	f	g

To Parents or Helpers:
   Using the Word Study Steps above as your child comes across any new words will help him or her spell well. Review the steps as you both go over this week's spelling words.
   Go over the Spelling Tip with your child. Ask if he or she knows other words that add -ed to tell about something in the past.
   Help your child find and circle the spelling words in the puzzle.

Words with Long e : ea, ie

Look at the words in the box.

reached   fields   read   sea   piece   leaf

Write the spelling words that have long **e** spelled **ea.**

1. _____   2. _____

3. _____   4. _____

Write the spelling words that have long **e** spelled **ie.**

5. _____   6. _____

Write the spelling word that ends with **ed.**

7. _____

Write the spelling word that ends with **s.**

8. _____

Words with Long e : ea, ie

Find the small word inside the bigger word. Circle
the small word.

1. fields

2. seas

3. pieces

4. reached

Look at the picture. Write the spelling word to
complete the sentence.

5. One field + one field
make two _____.

6. Fish swim in the _____.

7. A _____ is on a plant.

8. I like to _____ books.

9. Jon had one _____ of pie.

10. Mouse kept on running until
he _____ the woods.

Words with Long e : ea, ie

Finding Mistakes
Read the story. There are six spelling mistakes. Circle the mistakes. Write the words correctly on the lines.

Rabbit lived in the feelds near the woods. He liked to eat grass and a lefe or two from a plant. He also liked to eat a peece of carrot now and then. Rabbit hopped very fast. He hopped and hopped until he reched the see. It was very new to him, but he liked it. Now he wants to rede about it in a book.

1. _____   2. _____

3. _____   4. _____

5. _____   6. _____

Writing Activity
Write about Rabbit, Owl, or Mouse. Tell about something they did. Use at least two spelling words in your story.

_____

_____

_____

Words with Long e : ea, ie

Look at the words in each set. One word in each set is spelled correctly. Use a pencil to color in the circle in front of that word. Before you begin, look at the sample sets of words. Sample A has been done for you. Do Sample B by yourself. When you are sure you know what to do, you may go on with the rest of the page.

Sample A

(A) bead

(B) beed

(C) beade

Sample B

(D) shepe

(E) sheepe

(F) sheep

1. (A) reached

(B) reched

(C) reacht

2. (D) leaf

(E) leef

(F) laef

3. (A) rede

(B) reede

(C) read

4. (D) se

(E) sea

(F) shee

5. (A) peece

(B) piece

(C) pese

6. (D) fields

(E) feelds

(F) felds

Words with Long o: o, oa, oe, ow

Pretest Directions

Fold back the paper along the dotted line. Use the blanks to write each word as it is read aloud. When you finish the test, unfold the paper. Use the list at the right to correct any spelling mistakes. Practice the words you missed for the Posttest.

1. _____ 1. cold

2. _____ 2. goes

3. _____ 3. hold

4. _____ 4. road

5. _____ 5. show

6. _____ 6. boat

Challenge Words

_____ by

_____ kind

_____ more

_____ high

To Parents

Here are the results of your child's weekly spelling Pretest. You can help your child study for the Posttest by following these simple steps for each word on the list:

1. Read the word to your child.

2. Have your child write the word, saying each letter as it is written.

3. Say each letter of the word as your child checks the spelling.

4. If a mistake has been made, have your child read each letter of the correctly spelled word aloud, and then repeat steps 1-3.

Words with Long *o : o, oa, oe, ow*

Using the Word Study Steps

1. LOOK at the word.

2. SAY the word aloud.

3. STUDY the letters in the word.

4. WRITE the word.

5. CHECK the word.
   Did you spell the word right?
   If not, go back to step 1.

> **Spelling Tip**
>
> Use spell-check on a computer. Be careful! If you write a word that sounds like the word you need, spell-check will not catch the mistake.
>
> road   rode

Fill in the Blank

Write the spelling word that best fits each sentence.

1. I _____ the pen.

2. The _____ is on the lake.

3. _____ me the work.

4. I live on that _____.

5. It is _____ out.

6. She _____ to school.

To Parents or Helpers:
Using the Word Study Steps above as your child comes across any new words will help him or her spell well. Review the steps as you both go over this week's spelling words.
Go over the Spelling Tip with your child. Ask if he or she knows other sound-alike words. Help your child use a computer spell-check feature to learn that it will not catch mistakes in sound-alike words.
Help your child complete the spelling activity.

Words with Long o : o, oa, oe, ow

Look at the spelling words in the box.

| cold | goes | hold | road | show | boat |

Write the spelling words that have long **o** spelled **o.**

1. _____   2. _____

Write the spelling words that have long **o** spelled **oa.**

3. _____   4. _____

Write the spelling word that has long **o** spelled **oe.**

5. _____

Write the spelling word that has long **o** spelled **ow.**

6. _____

Circle the pairs that rhyme. Write the rhyming pairs.

| cold | road | show | goes | boat |
| hold | rod | grow | toes | bat |

7. _____   _____

8. _____   _____

9. _____   _____

Words with Long o : o, oa, oe, ow

Read the clue. Then write the spelling word that fits into the boxes in the puzzle. Put one letter in each box.

Down

1. Which word is the opposite of hot?

3. Which word rhymes with *toes*?

5. What means "to have in your hand"?

Across

2. What rides on water?

4. What do cars and trucks ride on?

6. You can see one of these on TV.

Book 1.5/Unit 1
You Can't Smell a Flower with Your Ear

Words with Long o : o, oa, oe, ow

Finding Mistakes
Read the sentences. One word in each sentence
has a spelling mistake. Circle each mistake. Write
the word correctly on the line.

1. Maria has a bad kold.

_____

2. I ride my bike on the roed.

_____

3. A bote can go across the sea.

_____

4. I took my cat to "Shoa and Tell."

_____

5. It was not fun to hoeld a wiggly cat.

_____

6. Mark goze to school every day.

_____

Writing Activity
Write a story about things you can do when the weather is
cold. Use three spelling words in your story.

_____

_____

_____

Words with Long o: o, oa, oe, ow

Look at the words in each set. One word in each set is spelled correctly. Use a pencil to color in the circle in front of that word. Before you begin, look at the sample sets of words. Sample A has been done for you. Do Sample B by yourself. When you are sure you know what to do, you may go on with the rest of the page.

Sample A
- (A) row
- (B) roa
- (C) rowe

Sample B
- (D) reade
- (E) raed
- (F) read

1. (A) knowd
   (B) kold
   (C) cold

4. (D) goes
   (E) goz
   (F) gose

2. (D) rowd
   (E) road
   (F) roade

5. (A) hold
   (B) howd
   (C) howld

3. (A) show
   (B) sho
   (C) shoow

6. (D) boat
   (E) bod
   (F) bot

Words with Long i: i, y, igh

Pretest Directions

Fold back the paper along the dotted line. Use the blanks to write each word as it is read aloud. When you finish the test, unfold the paper. Use the list at the right to correct any spelling mistakes. Practice the words you missed for the Posttest.

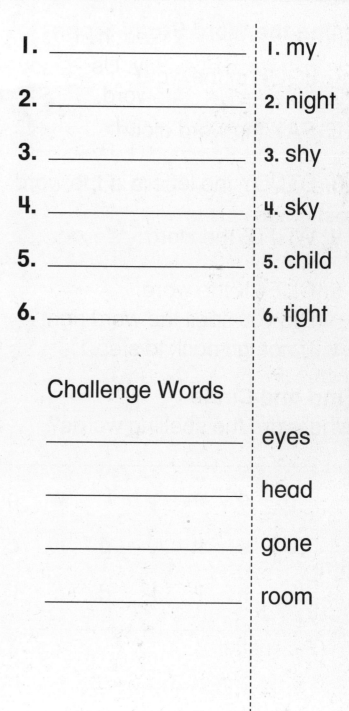

1. _____ 1. my

2. _____ 2. night

3. _____ 3. shy

4. _____ 4. sky

5. _____ 5. child

6. _____ 6. tight

Challenge Words

_____ eyes

_____ head

_____ gone

_____ room

To Parents

Here are the results of your child's weekly spelling Pretest. You can help your child study for the Posttest by following these simple steps for each word on the list:

1. Read the word to your child.

2. Have your child write the word, saying each letter as it is written.

3. Say each letter of the word as your child checks the spelling.

4. If a mistake has been made, have your child read each letter of the correctly spelled word aloud, and then repeat steps 1-3.

Words with Long *i : i, y, igh*

Using the Word Study Steps

1. LOOK at the word.

2. SAY the word aloud.

3. STUDY the letters in the word.

4. WRITE the word.

5. CHECK the word.
   Did you spell the word right?
   If not, go back to step 1.

<table>
<tr><td>Spelling Tip</td></tr>
<tr><td>Use beginnings and endings of words you can spell to help you spell new words.
shed + my = shy</td></tr>
</table>

Find and Circle

Where are the spelling words?

p	d	m	y	i	w	n	i	g	h	t
i	s	h	y	p	i	c	s	k	y	m
c	h	i	l	d	c	t	i	g	h	t

To Parents or Helpers:

Using the Word Study Steps above as your child comes across any new words will help him or her spell well. Review the steps as you both go over this week's spelling words.

Go over the Spelling Tip with your child. Help your child write new words that use beginnings and endings of words he or she can spell.

Help your child find and circle the spelling words in the puzzle.

Words with Long i : i, y, igh

Look at the spelling words in the box.

my	night	shy	sky	child	tight

Write the spelling word that has long **i** spelled **i**.

1. _____

Write the spelling words that have long **i** spelled **y**.

2. _____   3. _____

4. _____

Write the spelling words that have long **i** spelled **igh**.

5. _____   6. _____

Name_____ Date_____

Words with Long i : i, y, igh

Read this poem. Circle the five words in the poem
that end with **ight.** Then write two spelling words
that rhyme with the words you circled.

Star light, star bright

First star I see tonight

Wish I may, wish I might

Have the wish I wish tonight.

I. _____   2. _____

Write a spelling word to complete each sentence.

3. A boy or a girl is a _____.

4. Way up above us is the _____.

5. This doll belongs to me. It is _____ doll.

6. Joan is afraid to come out. She is very

_____.

7. We can see the stars at _____.

Words with Long i : i, y, igh

Finding Mistakes
Read the story. There are six spelling mistakes. Circle the mistakes. Write the correct words on the lines.

The childe looked at me. He gave his teddy bear a

tite hug. He was very shi and did not speak. I

hoped he would like mi gift. It was a book. It

showed all the stars in the nite skye. He said,

"Thank you."

1. _____   2. _____

3. _____   4. _____

5. _____   6. _____

Writing Activity
Do you like to look at the night sky? Write about the sky at night. Use two spelling words.

_____

_____

_____

Words with Long i : i, y, igh

Look at the words in each set. One word in each set is spelled correctly. Use a pencil to color in the circle in front of that word. Before you begin, look at the sample sets of words. Sample A has been done for you. Do Sample B by yourself. When you are sure you know what to do, you may go on with the rest of the page.

Sample A
- (A) right
- (B) rihgt
- (C) ryt

Sample B
- (D) hold
- (E) hoald
- (F) howld

1. (A) mi
   (B) my
   (C) mhy

2. (D) nite
   (E) niht
   (F) night

3. (A) shy
   (B) shi
   (C) shigh

4. (D) sky
   (E) skye
   (F) scy

5. (A) childe
   (B) cild
   (C) child

6. (D) tite
   (E) tiht
   (F) tight

Words from Science

Pretest Directions

Fold back the paper along the dotted line. Use the blanks to write each word as it is read aloud. When you finish the test, unfold the paper. Use the list at the right to correct any spelling mistakes. Practice the words you missed for the Posttest.

1. _____ 1. rat

2. _____ 2. bugs

3. _____ 3. owl

4. _____ 4. frog

5. _____ 5. logs

6. _____ 6. pond

Challenge Words

_____ many

_____ find

_____ come

_____ kinds

To Parents

Here are the results of your child's weekly spelling Pretest. You can help your child study for the Posttest by following these simple steps for each word on the list:

1. Read the word to your child.

2. Have your child write the word, saying each letter as it is written.

3. Say each letter of the word as your child checks the spelling.

4. If a mistake has been made, have your child read each letter of the correctly spelled word aloud, and then repeat steps 1-3.

Words from Science

Using the Word Study Steps

1. LOOK at the word.

2. SAY the word aloud.

3. STUDY the letters in the word.

4. WRITE the word.

5. CHECK the word.
    Did you spell the word right?
    If not, go back to step 1.

Spelling Tip

Add -s to most words to tell about more than one.

rat + **s** = rat**s**
bug + **s** = bug**s**

Word Scramble

Unscramble each set of letters to make a spelling word.

1. art _____   **2.** gosl _____

3. rfgo _____   **4.** wol _____

5. gbsu _____   **6.** npdo _____

To Parents or Helpers:
    Using the Word Study Steps above as your child comes across any new words will help him or her spell well. Review the steps as you both go over this week's spelling words.
    Go over the Spelling Tip with your child. Help your child add -s to words to tell about more than one.
    Help your child find and circle the spelling words in the puzzle.

Name_____ Date_____

Words from Science

Look at the spelling words in the box.

| rat | bugs | owl | frog | logs | pond |

Words that name more than one thing
usually end with **s.** Write the spelling
words that name more than one thing.

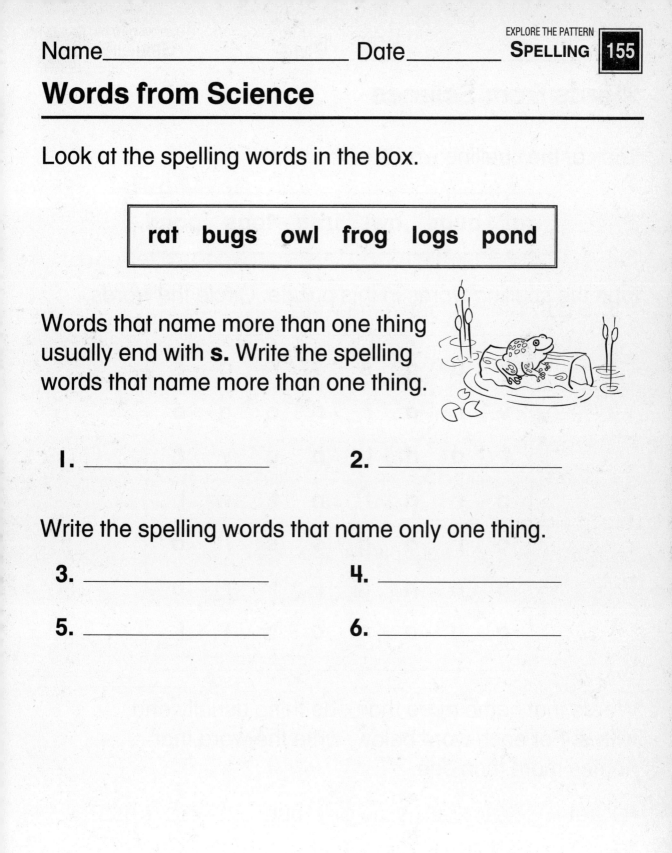

1. _____   2. _____

Write the spelling words that name only one thing.

3. _____   4. _____

5. _____   6. _____

Words from Science

Look at the spelling words in the box.

| rat | bugs | owl | frog | logs | pond |

Find the spelling words in this puzzle. Circle the words.

```
b  u  g  s  s  f  a  z
v  r  a  f  r  o  g  o
l  a  m  l  b  g  v  r
n  r  a  t  n  t  w  l
o  l  o  g  s  s  l  o
p  o  n  d  l  f  r  u
g  d  a  r  o  w  l  l
```

Words that name more than one thing usually end
with **s.** For each word below, write the word that
names more than one.

1. rat _____   4. bug _____

2. owl _____   5. log _____

3. frog _____   6. pond _____

Words from Science

Finding Mistakes
Read the letter. There are six spelling mistakes. Circle the mistakes. Write the words correctly on the lines.

Dear Mom and Dad,

I am having fun at camp. We swim in a pand every day. There are froggs in the pond. I like them. They eat bugz. We went on a hike at night. I saw an owle sitting on a logg. It jumped down when a ratt went by.

Love,

Willy

1. _____   2. _____

3. _____   4. _____

5. _____   6. _____

Writing Activity
Write about something that you can do at camp.
Use two spelling words.

_____

_____

_____

Words from Science

Look at the words in each set. One word in each set is spelled correctly. Use a pencil to color in the circle in front of that word. Before you begin, look at the sample sets of words. Sample A has been done for you. Do Sample B by yourself. When you are sure you know what to do, you may go on with the rest of the page.

Sample A
- (A) fields
- (B) feilds
- (C) feelds

Sample B
- (D) skie
- (E) skigh
- (F) sky

1. (A) logs
   (B) logz
   (C) loogs

4. (D) frogge
   (E) frogg
   (F) frog

2. (D) pand
   (E) ponde
   (F) pond

5. (A) ratt
   (B) ratte
   (C) rat

3. (A) owle
   (B) owl
   (C) owel

6. (D) bugs
   (E) bugz
   (F) buggs

Book 1.5/Unit 1 Review Test

Read each sentence. If an underlined word is spelled wrong, fill in the circle that goes with that word. If no word is spelled wrong, fill in the circle below NONE.

Read Sample A, and do Sample B.

A. I <u>hope</u> it will not <u>raine</u> that <u>day</u>.
      A   B   C

NONE
A. Ⓐ ⬤B Ⓒ Ⓓ

B. He will <u>hide</u> the <u>ring</u> at <u>houme</u>.
          E   F   G

NONE
B. Ⓔ Ⓕ Ⓖ Ⓗ

1. <u>Shee</u> will see the <u>bugs</u> on the <u>pond</u>.
    A   B   C

NONE
1. Ⓐ Ⓑ Ⓒ Ⓓ

2. The <u>child</u> has a <u>peece</u> to <u>show</u>.
       E   F   G

NONE
2. Ⓔ Ⓕ Ⓖ Ⓗ

3. At <u>nyght</u> the <u>owl</u> came to the <u>pond</u>.
      A   B   C

NONE
3. Ⓐ Ⓑ Ⓒ Ⓓ

4. There are <u>buges</u> on the <u>cold</u> <u>road</u>.
          E   F G

NONE
4. Ⓔ Ⓕ Ⓖ Ⓗ

5. The <u>child</u> saw two <u>bugs</u> in the <u>ponnd</u>.
       A   B   C

NONE
5. Ⓐ Ⓑ Ⓒ Ⓓ

6. The <u>seaa</u> is <u>cold</u> at <u>night</u>.
      E   F   G

NONE
6. Ⓔ Ⓕ Ⓖ Ⓗ

Go on ➡

7. <u>She</u> feels <u>colde</u> by the <u>pond</u>.
    A   B   C

NONE
7. Ⓐ Ⓑ Ⓒ Ⓓ

8. This <u>roade</u> can be <u>reached</u> from the <u>pond</u>.
         E   F   G

NONE
8. Ⓔ Ⓕ Ⓖ Ⓗ

9. We felt the <u>cold</u> <u>skie</u> by the <u>sea</u>.
            A   B   C

NONE
9. Ⓐ Ⓑ Ⓒ Ⓓ

10. The <u>child</u> <u>reached</u> for the <u>owle</u>.
       E   F   G

NONE
10. Ⓔ Ⓕ Ⓖ Ⓗ

11. Does <u>she</u> hear a <u>bea</u> by the <u>pond</u>?
          A   B   C

NONE
11. Ⓐ Ⓑ Ⓒ Ⓓ

12. Mom <u>reachd</u> for the <u>cold</u> <u>child</u>.
        E   F   G

NONE
12. Ⓔ Ⓕ Ⓖ Ⓗ

13. They did not <u>show</u> the <u>bee</u> or the <u>bugs</u>.
          A   B   C

NONE
13. Ⓐ Ⓑ Ⓒ Ⓓ

14. The <u>childe</u> <u>reached</u> for the <u>sky</u>.
      E   F   G

NONE
14. Ⓔ Ⓕ Ⓖ Ⓗ

15. Did <u>she</u> see a <u>sheepe</u> at the <u>show</u>?
      A   B   C

NONE
15. Ⓐ Ⓑ Ⓒ Ⓓ

Words with /ü/oo

Pretest Directions

Fold back the paper along the dotted line. Use the blanks to write each word as it is read aloud. When you finish the test, unfold the paper. Use the list at the right to correct any spelling mistakes. Practice the words you missed for the Posttest.

1. _____
2. _____
3. _____
4. _____
5. _____
6. _____

1. roof
2. fool
3. zoo
4. soon
5. cool
6. moon

Challenge Words

_____ these

_____ called

_____ only

_____ friend

To Parents

Here are the results of your child's weekly spelling Pretest. You can help your child study for the Posttest by following these simple steps for each word on the list:

1. Read the word to your child.

2. Have your child write the word, saying each letter as it is written.

3. Say each letter of the word as your child checks the spelling.

4. If a mistake has been made, have your child read each letter of the correctly spelled word aloud, and then repeat steps 1-3.

Words with /ü/oo

Using the Word Study Steps

1. LOOK at the word.

2. SAY the word aloud.

3. STUDY the letters in the word.

4. WRITE the word.

5. CHECK the word.
   Did you spell the word right?
   If not, go back to step 1.

Find and Circle
Where are the spelling words?

Spelling Tip

Think of times when you have seen the word. Maybe you have read it in a book or on a sign. Try to remember how it looked. Write the word in different ways to see which one looks correct.

~~mun~~ ~~mune~~ moon

```
r   o   o   f   c   u   f   o   o   l   r
o   d   z   o   o   p   r   s   o   o   n
r   c   o   o   l   h   m   o   o   n   g
```

To Parents or Helpers:
    Using the Word Study Steps above as your child comes across any new words will help him or her spell well. Review the steps as you both go over this week's spelling words.
    Go over the Spelling Tip with your child. Ask if he or she knows other sound-alike words.
    Help your child complete the spelling activity.

Words with /ü/oo

Look at the spelling words in the box.

roof fool zoo soon cool moon

Write the spelling words that end with **oon.**

1. _____   2. _____

Write the spelling words that end with **ool.**

3. _____   4. _____

Write the word that ends with **oo.**

5. _____

Write the word that ends with **oof.**

6. _____

Circle the pairs that rhyme. Write the pairs.

fool	soon	roof	tool	zoo
cool	moon	boot	school	so

7. _____   _____

8. _____   _____

9. _____   _____

Words with /ü/oo

Complete each sentence with a spelling word.

1. The top of a house is the r_____.

2. Many animals live in a z_____.

3. Tonight, the m_____ is bright and round.

4. The opposite of warm is c_____.

5. A word that means "before long" is s_____.

6. A word that means "to trick someone" is f_____.

Look at the spelling words in the box. Find the
words in the puzzle.

roof	fool	zoo	soon	cool	moon

o	s	o	o	n	o	o	l
c	o	m	o	o	n	o	f
c	o	o	l	o	s	o	m
o	o	n	o	f	o	o	l
z	o	z	o	o	o	f	o
o	o	r	o	r	o	o	f

Words with /ü/oo

Finding Mistakes
Read the sentences. There is one spelling mistake
in each sentence. Circle each mistake. Write the
word correctly on the line.

1. The rufe is at the top of our house. _____

2. The mune shines in the night sky. _____

3. You cannot fol me! I know it is a trick! _____

4. Bears live in the woods and in a zu. _____

5. It was warm, but now it is kool. _____

6. I will come as sune as I can. _____

Writing Activity
Write about a trip to the zoo. What is the zoo like?
Use two spelling words.

_____

_____

_____

Words with /ü/oo

Look at the words in each set. One word in each set is spelled correctly. Use a pencil to color in the circle in front of that word. Before you begin, look at the sample sets of words. Sample A has been done for you. Do Sample B by yourself. When you are sure you know what to do, you may go on with the rest of the page.

Sample A

(A) pool

(B) pul

(C) pol

Sample B

(D) skie

(E) sky

(F) skigh

1. (A) zuw

(B) zoo

(C) zou

4. (D) moun

(E) moon

(F) mun

2. (D) ful

(E) foole

(F) fool

5. (A) cool

(B) kool

(C) koul

3. (A) rofe

(B) roofe

(C) roof

6. (D) soone

(E) soon

(F) sune

Book 1.5/Unit 2
A Friend for Little Bear

Words with /är/ar

Pretest Directions

Fold back the paper along the dotted line. Use the blanks to write each word as it is read aloud. When you finish the test, unfold the paper. Use the list at the right to correct any spelling mistakes. Practice the words you missed for the Posttest.

1. _____
2. _____
3. _____
4. _____
5. _____
6. _____

1. car
2. bark
3. star
4. dark
5. part
6. park

Challenge Words

_____ every

_____ or

_____ took

_____ morning

To Parents

Here are the results of your child's weekly spelling Pretest. You can help your child study for the Posttest by following these simple steps for each word on the list:

1. Read the word to your child.

2. Have your child write the word, saying each letter as it is written.

3. Say each letter of the word as your child checks the spelling.

4. If a mistake has been made, have your child read each letter of the correctly spelled word aloud, and then repeat steps 1-3.

Name_____ Date_____

Words with /är/ar

Using the Word Study Steps

1. LOOK at the word.

2. SAY the word aloud.

3. STUDY the letters in the word.

4. WRITE the word.

5. CHECK the word.
   Did you spell the word right?
   If not, go back to step 1.

Spelling Tip

Rhyming words are often spelled alike. A word you know can help you spell a new word.

c + ar = car
st + ar = star

X the Word

In each row, X the word that does not belong.

1.	car	hop	bus
2.	dog	bark	trip
3.	star	far	tack
4.	big	part	cart
5.	dark	pet	light
6.	win	park	pin

To Parents or Helpers:
   Using the Word Study Steps above as your child comes across any new words will help him or her spell well. Review the steps as you both go over this week's spelling words.
   Go over the Spelling Tip with your child. Ask if he or she knows other words that rhyme with the spelling words.
   Help your child complete the spelling activity .

Words with /är/ar

Look at the words in the box.

car bark star part dark park

Write the words that end with **ar**.

1. _____ 2. _____

Write the word that ends with **art**.

3. _____

Write the words that end with **ark**.

4. _____ 5. _____ 6. _____

These spelling words are scrambled. Put the letters in the right order. Write the spelling word on each line.

7. rac _____ 8. krab _____

9. krad _____ 10. pkra _____

11. sart _____ 12. tpar _____

Words with /är/ar

Add **ed** to the end of these spelling words.

1. bark _____

2. park _____

Find the small word inside the bigger word. Circle the small word.

3. cars   **4.** barked   **5.** stars   **6.** barks

7. parts   **8.** parked   **9.** parks

Complete each sentence with a spelling word.

10. We like to ride in the _____.

11. Make a wish upon a _____.

12. The sound a dog makes is called a _____.

13. The opposite of light is _____.

14. We go to the _____ to play games.

15. What _____ of the book did you like best?

Words with /är/ar

Finding Mistakes
Read the rhymes. There are five spelling mistakes. Circle the mistakes. Write the words correctly on the lines.

We are going to the parc.
The dog is happy. Hear her barc!

1. _____

2. _____

We will play until it's darck.
Then we'll have to leave the park.

3. _____

We will wish upon a starr,
And then we'll drive home in the kar.

4. _____

5. _____

Writing Activity
Write about a trip to a park. Use three spelling words.

_____

_____

_____

Words with /är/ar

Look at the words in each set. One word in each set is spelled correctly. Use a pencil to color in the circle in front of that word. Before you begin, look at the sample sets of words. Sample A has been done for you. Do Sample B by yourself. When you are sure you know what to do, you may go on with the rest of the page.

Sample A
- (A) far
- (B) faar
- (C) farr

Sample B
- (D) foole
- (E) ful
- (F) fool

1. (A) kar
   (B) car
   (C) caar

4. (D) paht
   (E) parte
   (F) part

2. (D) bark
   (E) barc
   (F) barch

5. (A) starr
   (B) star
   (C) sar

3. (A) dahk
   (B) dak
   (C) dark

6. (D) park
   (E) pak
   (F) pahk

Words with /ûr/ ir, ur, er

Pretest Directions

Fold back the paper along the dotted line. Use the blanks to write each word as it is read aloud. When you finish the test, unfold the paper. Use the list at the right to correct any spelling mistakes. Practice the words you missed for the Posttest.

1. _____ 1. bird

2. _____ 2. burn

3. _____ 3. girl

4. _____ 4. serve

5. _____ 5. hurt

6. _____ 6. first

Challenge Words

_____ from

_____ sister

_____ mother

_____ brother

To Parents

Here are the results of your child's weekly spelling Pretest. You can help your child study for the Posttest by following these simple steps for each word on the list:

1. Read the word to your child.

2. Have your child write the word, saying each letter as it is written.

3. Say each letter of the word as your child checks the spelling.

4. If a mistake has been made, have your child read each letter of the correctly spelled word aloud, and then repeat steps 1-3.

Words with /ûr/ ir, ur, er

Using the Word Study Steps

1. LOOK at the word.

2. SAY the word aloud.

3. STUDY the letters in the word.

4. WRITE the word.

5. CHECK the word.
   Did you spell the word right?
   If not, go back to step 1.

Spelling Tip

No English words end in **j**, **q**, or **v**.

Word Scramble

Unscramble each set of letters to make a spelling word.

1. dibr _____   2. rhtu _____

3. eevrs _____   4. glri _____

5. rbnu _____   6. isfrt _____

To Parents or Helpers:
Using the Word Study Steps above as your child comes across any new words will help him or her spell well. Review the steps as you both go over this week's spelling words.
Go over the Spelling Tip with your child. Ask your child if the word **serve** follows this rule. Help your child complete the spelling activity.

Words with /ûr/ ir, ur, er

Look at the spelling words in the box.

bird burn girl serve hurt first

Write the words with **ir.**

1. _____   2. _____

3. _____

Write the words with **ur.**

4. _____   5. _____

Write the word with **er.**

6. _____

These spelling words are scrambled. Put the letters in the right order. Write the spelling word on each line.

7. drib _____   8. nrub _____

9. rigl _____   10. rtuh _____

11. strif _____   12. ersev _____

Words with /ûr/ ir, ur, er

Find the small word inside the bigger word. Circle the small word.

1. girls   **2.** burned

3. hurts   **4.** birds

Complete each sentence with a spelling word.

5. A _____ likes to fly high and low.

6. The opposite of boy is _____.

7. If you bump your head, it might _____.

8. New Year's Day is the _____ day of the year.

9. The logs will _____ in the fire.

10. The waiter will _____ the food.

Words with /ûr/ ir, ur, er

Finding Mistakes
Read the story. There are six spelling mistakes.
Circle the mistakes. Write the words correctly on
the lines.

A gerl named Rose had a blue berd. She found it in

the park. The bird was hert. It had a birn on its

wing. Rose helped to make it well again. Furst, she

sirved the bird seeds and other good food. Then

she let it fly away home.

I. _____ 2. _____

3. _____ 4. _____

5. _____ 6. _____

Writing Activity
Write a story about a girl and a bird. Use two
spelling words.

_____

_____

_____

Words with /ûr/ ir, ur, er

Look at the words in each set. One word in each set is spelled correctly. Use a pencil to color in the circle in front of that word. Before you begin, look at the sample sets of words. Sample A has been done for you. Do Sample B by yourself. When you are sure you know what to do, you may go on with the rest of the page.

Sample A
- (A) turn
- (B) tern
- (C) tirn

Sample B
- (D) starr
- (E) star
- (F) staar

1. (A) girl
   (B) gerl
   (C) gurl

4. (D) first
   (E) ferst
   (F) furst

2. (D) birn
   (E) bern
   (F) burn

5. (A) berd
   (B) bird
   (C) burd

3. (A) hirt
   (B) hert
   (C) hurt

6. (D) sirve
   (E) serve
   (F) surve

Words with /ou/ow, ou; /oi/oi, oy

Pretest Directions
Fold back the paper along the dotted line. Use the blanks to write each word as it is read aloud. When you finish the test, unfold the paper. Use the list at the right to correct any spelling mistakes. Practice the words you missed for the Posttest.

1. _____ 1. boys
2. _____ 2. mouse
3. _____ 3. toy
4. _____ 4. noise
5. _____ 5. sound
6. _____ 6. town

Challenge Words

_____ people

_____ father

_____ should

_____ horse

To Parents
Here are the results of your child's weekly spelling Pretest. You can help your child study for the Posttest by following these simple steps for each word on the list:

1. Read the word to your child.

2. Have your child write the word, saying each letter as it is written.

3. Say each letter of the word as your child checks the spelling.

4. If a mistake has been made, have your child read each letter of the correctly spelled word aloud, and then repeat steps 1-3.

Words with /ou/*ow, ow*; /oi/*oi, oy*

Using the Word Study Steps

1. LOOK at the word.

2. SAY the word aloud.

3. STUDY the letters in the word.

4. WRITE the word.

5. CHECK the word.
   Did you spell the word right?
   If not, go back to step 1.

Spelling Tip

Add -s to most words to tell about more than one.

boy + **s** = boy**s**

Find and Circle
Where are the spelling words?

b	o	y	s	y	m	o	u	s	e	t
t	n	t	o	y	e	n	o	i	s	e
s	s	o	u	n	d	h	t	o	w	n

To Parents or Helpers:
Using the Word Study Steps above as your child comes across any new words will help him or her spell well. Review the steps as you both go over this week's spelling words.
Go over the Spelling Tip with your child. Help your child write new words that use beginnings and endings of words he or she can spell.
Help your child find and circle the spelling words in the puzzle.

Words with /ou/ow, ou; /oi/oi, oy

Look at the spelling words in the box.

boys   mouse   toy   noise   sound   town

Find the spelling words with each of the spellings below. Write each word in the correct mouse.

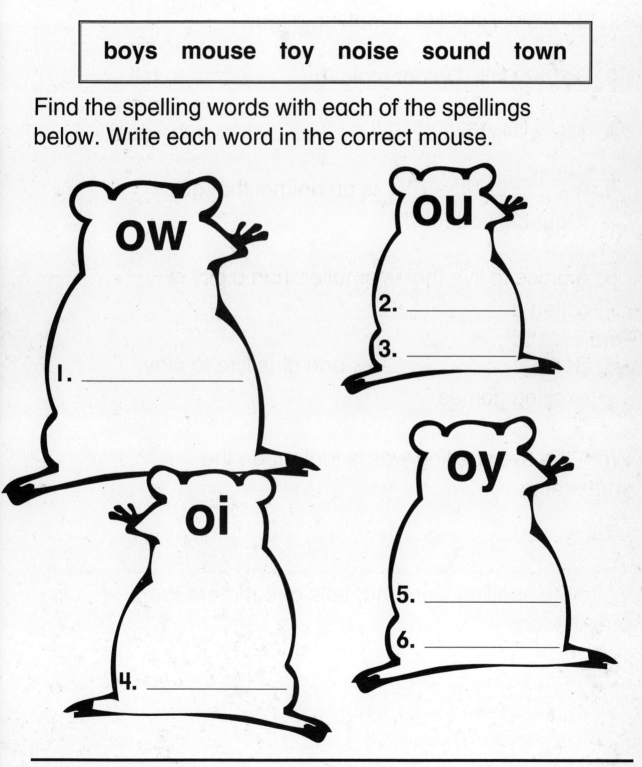

ow

ou

2. _____

3. _____

1. _____

oi

oy

5. _____

6. _____

4. _____

Words with /ou/*ow, ou;* /oi/*oi, oy*

Write a spelling word to complete each sentence.

1. Billy is yelling. He is making a loud _____.

2. Be very still. Do not make a _____.

3. My doll is the _____ I love the best.

4. A _____ is an animal that goes "Squeak, squeak!"

5. A place to live that is smaller than a city is called a _____.

6. Both _____ and girls like to play exciting games.

Write the two spelling words that mean the same thing.

7. _____   _____

Write the spelling word that tells about more than one person.

8. _____

Words with /ou/ow, ou; /oi/oi, oy

Finding Mistakes
Read the story. There are six spelling mistakes. Circle the mistakes. Write the words correctly on the lines.

In a small towne, there lived two boys.

They were good friends. They played

games together. Their best toi was a

fake mous. It made sownds like a real

mouse. The boyz also liked to make

noyse with the horns on their bikes.

They had lots of good times together.

1. _____   2. _____

3. _____   4. _____

5. _____   6. _____

Writing Activity
Write a story about something you would like to do with a good friend. Use three spelling words.

_____

_____

_____

Words with /ou/ow, ou; /oi/oi, oy

Look at the words in each set. One word in each set is spelled correctly. Use a pencil to color in the circle in front of that word. Before you begin, look at the sample sets of words. Sample A has been done for you. Do Sample B by yourself. When you are sure you know what to do, you may go on with the rest of the page.

Sample A

Ⓐ down
Ⓑ doun
Ⓒ downe

Sample B

Ⓓ girl
Ⓔ gerl
Ⓕ gurl

1. Ⓐ sond
   Ⓑ sound
   Ⓒ sownd

2. Ⓓ noyse
   Ⓔ noize
   Ⓕ noise

3. Ⓐ toy
   Ⓑ toi
   Ⓒ towy

4. Ⓓ mouse
   Ⓔ mous
   Ⓕ mowse

5. Ⓐ boyz
   Ⓑ bois
   Ⓒ boys

6. Ⓓ town
   Ⓔ toun
   Ⓕ towne

Words from Math

Pretest Directions

Fold back the paper along the dotted line. Use the blanks to write each word as it is read aloud. When you finish the test, unfold the paper. Use the list at the right to correct any spelling mistakes. Practice the words you missed for the Posttest.

1. _____   1. ten

2. _____   2. five

3. _____   3. less

4. _____   4. feet

5. _____   5. sum

6. _____   6. miles

Challenge Words

_____   from

_____   these

_____   people

_____   horses

To Parents

Here are the results of your child's weekly spelling Pretest. You can help your child study for the Posttest by following these simple steps for each word on the list:

1. Read the word to your child.

2. Have your child write the word, saying each letter as it is written.

3. Say each letter of the word as your child checks the spelling.

4. If a mistake has been made, have your child read each letter of the correctly spelled word aloud, and then repeat steps 1-3.

Words from Math

Using the Word Study Steps

1. LOOK at the word.

2. SAY the word aloud.

3. STUDY the letters in the word.

4. WRITE the word.

5. CHECK the word.
   Did you spell the word right?
   If not, go back to step 1.

> **Spelling Tip**
>
> Add -s to most words to tell about more than one.
> rat + **s** = rat**s**
> bug + **s** = bug**s**

Fill in the Blank

Write the spelling word that best fits each sentence.

1. This year's snow was _____ than four inches.

2. He lives three _____ from here.

3. The pool is eight _____ deep.

4. I have _____ fingers on one hand.

5. _____ minus one is nine.

6. The _____ of four and three is seven.

To Parents or Helpers:
    Using the Word Study Steps above as your child comes across any new words will help him or her spell well. Review the steps as you both go over this week's spelling words.
    Go over the Spelling Tip with your child. Help your child add -s to words to tell about more than one.
    Help your child fill in the missing words.

Words from Math

Look at the spelling words in the box.

ten	five	less	feet	sum	miles

Write the spelling word that rhymes with each word below.

1. dress _____

2. dive _____

3. meat _____

4. smiles _____

5. when _____

6. come _____

Write the spelling words that have short vowel sounds.

7. _____ **8.** _____

9. _____

Write the spelling words that have long vowel sounds.

10. _____ **11.** _____

12. _____

Words from Math

Write the spelling word that answers each question.

1. Which word tells the number of fingers you have on each hand?

_____

2. Which word tells how many toes you have all together? _____

3. You know that 12 inches is one foot. Which word means more than one foot?

_____

4. Which word means two numbers added together? _____

$$2+3=5$$

5. You can walk one mile. Which word means more than one mile?

_____

New York 10

6. Which word means the opposite of more?

_____

Words from Math

Finding Mistakes

Read the sentences. Find the spelling mistake in each sentence. Circle the mistake. Write the correct word on the line.

1. I walked two milez to school. _____

2. There are fiv stars in the sky. _____

3. Two is lesse than three. _____

4. The som of three and three is six. _____

5. There are tenn boys in the class. _____

6. Wipe your feete on the mat. _____

Writing Activity

Write a math word problem. Use two spelling words.

_____

_____

_____

Words from Math

Look at the words in each set. One word in each set is spelled correctly. Use a pencil to color in the circle in front of that word. Before you begin, look at the sample sets of words. Sample A has been done for you. Do Sample B by yourself. When you are sure you know what to do, you may go on with the rest of the page.

Sample A
- (A) white
- (B) wite
- (C) hwite

Sample B
- (D) toi
- (E) toy
- (F) tyoi

1.
- (A) summ
- (B) sum
- (C) som

2.
- (D) fet
- (E) feet
- (F) feete

3.
- (A) less
- (B) lws
- (C) lesse

4.
- (D) five
- (E) fiv
- (F) fyv

5.
- (A) tenn
- (B) tenne
- (C) ten

6.
- (D) milez
- (E) miles
- (F) mils

Book 1.5/Unit 2 Review Test

Read each sentence. If an underlined word is spelled wrong, fill in the circle that goes with that word. If no word is spelled wrong, fill in the circle below NONE.

Read Sample A, and do Sample B.

A. The <u>road</u> at <u>nyght</u> was <u>cold</u>.
      A   B   C

NONE
A. (A) (●) (C) (D)

B. When had the <u>owl</u> <u>reached</u> the <u>sea</u>?
             E   F   G

NONE
B. (E) (F) (G) (H)

1. The <u>starr</u> and <u>moon</u> shine in the <u>dark</u>.
      A   B   C

NONE
1. (A) (B) (C) (D)

2. We can <u>foole</u> the <u>boys</u> with a <u>noise</u>.
        E   F   G

NONE
2. (E) (F) (G) (H)

3. The <u>byrd</u> makes a <u>noise</u> under the <u>moon</u>.
      A   B   C

NONE
3. (A) (B) (C) (D)

4. Let me <u>serfe</u> the <u>ten</u> <u>boys</u>.
        E   F G

NONE
4. (E) (F) (G) (H)

5. That <u>part</u> of the <u>moon</u> is <u>darck</u>.
      A   B   C

NONE
5. (A) (B) (C) (D)

6. The <u>boys</u> saw a new <u>bird</u> at the <u>zooe</u>.
      E   F   G

NONE
6. (E) (F) (G) (H)

Go on →

7. The <u>mowse</u> can <u>fool</u> the <u>bird</u>.
      A   B   C

NONE
7. Ⓐ Ⓑ Ⓒ Ⓓ

8. The <u>boys</u> have the <u>summ</u> to buy a <u>mouse</u>.
      E   F   G

NONE
8. Ⓔ Ⓕ Ⓖ Ⓗ

9. The <u>fool</u> has <u>parte</u> of the <u>ten</u> cookies.
      A   B   C

NONE
9. Ⓐ Ⓑ Ⓒ Ⓓ

10. The <u>star</u> seems to <u>burrn</u> near the <u>moon</u>.
       E   F   G

NONE
10. Ⓔ Ⓕ Ⓖ Ⓗ

11. <u>Ten</u> <u>boyz</u> will make a lot of <u>noise</u>.
     A B   C

NONE
11. Ⓐ Ⓑ Ⓒ Ⓓ

12. There are <u>fyv</u> boys <u>under</u> the <u>star</u>.
         E   F   G

NONE
12. Ⓔ Ⓕ Ⓖ Ⓗ

13. The <u>bird</u> at the <u>zoo</u> looks at the <u>moone</u>.
      A   B   C

NONE
13. Ⓐ Ⓑ Ⓒ Ⓓ

14. There is a <u>noyze</u> in the <u>dark</u> <u>zoo</u>.
          E   F G

NONE
14. Ⓔ Ⓕ Ⓖ Ⓗ

15. <u>Ten</u> will be <u>part</u> of the <u>sum</u>.
     A   B   C

NONE
15. Ⓐ Ⓑ Ⓒ Ⓓ